Your safe and trusted community.

What the **METAVERSE** is and How it Will Shape Your Future

TYRONE D. TABORN

PUBLISHED BY STEM CITY PRESS

www.stemcityusa.com

STEM City Press
729 E. Pratt Street, Ste. 504
Baltimore, MD 21202

First STEM City Press edition December 2022

STEM City Press and Metaquake USA are registered Trademarks of Career Communications Group, Inc.

For information about special discounts or Bulk purchases, please contact Career Communications Group, Inc. at 410-244-7101 or wecare@ccgmag.com

Library of Congress Cataloging-in-Publication Data
ISBN: 978-0-9624899-1-4

A change is coming, and today is the tomorrow that started yesterday.

PREFACE

The world faces another massive shift: a technology earthquake. In every previous tech revolution, Black people and other minorities have been losers. Will the metaverse be the opportunity to even the playing field? This book, Metaquake USA, will address that question through the voices of people who have laid the foundation for the metaverse. The "Metaquake USA with Tyrone Taborn" show on STEM City USA featured voices like Mark Dean, part of the team that created the IBM personal computer; Jesse Russell, who created the concept for the wireless digital phone and communication while working as an engineer at AT&T Bell Laboratories; and James West, who developed the mic (officially known as the electroacoustic transducer electret microphone) while with Bell Laboratories.

Our discussions show how the building blocks that people like Dean, Russell, and West pioneered came together to help change how we use our computers and phones. Through their stories, we trace the journey from the old telephone set to your advanced smartphone, which has a phone, a camera, a music player, and other digital applications in one device.

When the pandemic hit, it was devastating. Well, at Career Communications Group, we had already been on a significant resetting path. We were not simply trying to bridge the digital divide; we were bringing people together online for distance learning, training, meetings, and community experiences. So, we said, "What happens if a snowstorm hits us again? What happens if there's a terrorist attack? How can we continue building this trusted community we created if we can't all physically get together?"

In March 2020, leading technologists, educators, and business leaders came together to build STEM City USA. STEM City is about energy and soul renewal. It is more than a digital world. You can almost feel the power of live cultural events, music, and theater. STEM City promises a better future for children with caring mentors and hands-on activities with dedicated tutors. STEM City is your passport to a healthy lifestyle with weekly events addressing our issues. STEM City is your financial well-being with helpful information on wealth management, career advancement, job training, etc. STEM City is the community you deserve. It is the city where your dreams can come true. STEM City USA is accessible to all who reach for the stars in the sky.

STEM City Founders

Our mission is to establish the community under the leadership of 12 industry leaders and influencers that bring diversity of thought, talent, and impact to STEM City USA and the participants.

William Brown, SES (Ret.) Chairman

A retired industry executive and senior U.S. Army Corps of Engineers executive, William Brown served on the Industry Advisory Group of the U.S. State Department and has directed, planned, and designed construction projects and programs in Russia, Hungary, Nigeria, and France. He led asite planning study for the National Museum of African American History and Culture in Washington, D.C.; has lectured at several colleges and universities in the United States; and received numerous awards and recognitions. Currently, he is chairman of Hampton University's School of Engineering Advisory Board for Aviation, Architecture, Engineering, and Technology. 2000 BEYA Professional Achievement.

Lt. General Bruce Crawford (Ret.)

A decorated combat veteran, Bruce Crawford served as principal enterprise information technology (IT) and cyber security policy advisor to the United States Army and held various operational and strategic leadership positions in North America, Europe, the Pacific, and Southwest Asia. With Jacobs Engineering Group Inc. since 2020, Crawford brings more than 34 years of executive management in national security, enterprise IT, and cyber security as the senior vice president of strategic development in Jacobs' Critical Mission Solutions. Crawford holds a Bachelor of Science in electrical engineering and a Master of Science in administration and national resource strategy. He is the 2020 Black Engineer of the Year.

President Darryll J. Pines

Darryll J. Pines serves as president of the University of Maryland (UMD) and the Glenn L. Martin Professor of Aerospace Engineering. He was formerly the Nariman Farvard Professor of Engineering and dean of UMD's A. James Clark School of Engineering, where he has been on the faculty since 1995. As dean, Pines instituted changes to improve the student experience, including revamping teaching in fundamental undergraduate courses, encouraging participation in national and international student competitions, emphasizing sustainability engineering and service-learning, and expanding innovation and entrepreneurship activities. In 2019, he was elected to the National Academy of Engineering for his "inspirational leadership and contributions to engineering education."

Dr. Melvin Greer

Melvin Greer is chief data scientist, Americas, Intel Corporation. He is responsible for building Intel's data science platform through artificial intelligence, machine learning, blockchain zerotrust models, and neuromorphic computing to accelerate data transformation into a strategic asset for global enterprises. His systems and software engineering experience have resulted in patented inventions in cloud computing, synthetic biology, and Internet of Things biosensors for edge analytics. Greer received the 2012 BEYA Technologist of the Year Award, which recognizes his outstanding technical contributions that have had a material impact and high value on society. He is a member of the AAAS and the National Academy of Science, Engineering, and Medicine. He functions as a university professor and principal investigator, where he significantly advances the body of knowledge in basic research and advanced engineering. Greer is an award-winning author of five books, and the managing director of the Greer Institute for Leadership and Innovation focused on the maturing of new leaders and the growth of future innovators.

Dr. Linda R. Gooden, h.c.

The University System of Maryland (USM) Board of Regents elected Linda R. Gooden as its chair in 2018. A champion for math, science, and technology education, she has served on executive boards for the University of Maryland A. James Clark School of Engineering and Robert H. Smith School of Business Center for Electronic Markets & Enterprises, University of Maryland, Baltimore County, and Prince Georges' Community College Foundation, as well as the Maryland Business Roundtable for Education. Gooden also serves on civic and business leadership boards, such as the Eisenhower Fellowships program, AFCEA International, and the American Heart Association. A retired executive vice president of Lockheed Martin Information Systems & Global Services, she currently serves as a board member at General Motors, Home Depot, WGL, and ADP, Inc. Her many awards include the 2006 Black Engineer of the Year Award.

Dr. Victor R. McCrary

Victor McCrary is currently vice president for research and graduate Programs at the University of the District of Columbia. Before this position, he was vice chancellor for research at the University of Tennessee, Knoxville. Before that, he was the first vice president for research and economic development at Morgan State University. Previously, he was the business area executive for science & technology at The Johns Hopkins University Applied Physics Laboratory (APL). He is a former national president of the National Organization for the Professional Advancement of Black Chemists and Chemical Engineers (NOBCChE) and an American Chemical Society fellow. In 2011, he was honored as

Scientist of the Year by the BEYA STEM Conference. McCrary is a member of the National Science Board's class of 2016–2022.

Krystal Porter

Krystal Porter is a lead engineer and solutions architect at Leidos. She is also the chief financial officer of the Black Cybersecurity Association. She has extensive experience in solving complex architecture challenges for defense systems and missions by leveraging internal and external resources for optimal results. She leads and serves in multi-discipline teams at geographically dispersed locations with maximum resiliency to support those systems and missions. She is a passionate, results-oriented leader focused on innovation, integrated and multi-channel solutions to deliver customer loyalty and profitable growth. Porter is the 2021winner of the BEYA Dr. Wanda M. Austin Legacy Award.

Dr. Kevin T. Kornegay

Presently a professor and IoT security endowed chair in the Electrical & Computer Engineering department at Morgan State University, Dr. Kevin Kornegay's interests include reverse engineering, hardware assurance, secure embedded system design, radio frequency and millimeter-wave integrated circuit design, high-speed circuits, broadband wired and wireless communication systems, and cyber-physical systems. He has served on the technical program committees of several international conferences and symposia, including the IEEE Symposium on Hardware-Oriented Security and Trust, IEEE International Solid-State Circuits Conference, the IEEE Customs Integrated Circuits Conference, and the Radio Frequency Integrated Circuits Symposium. Kornegay was the 2002 Black Engineer of the Year Award in Higher Education.

Dr. John Brooks Slaughter

In January 2021, the University of Southern California (USC) Rossier School of Education and USC Viterbi School of Engineering announced Dr. John Brooks Slaughter's appointment as the Deans'

Professor of Education and Engineering. Slaughter's leadership has impacted efforts such as the American Society for Engineering Education Deans Diversity Pledge. Engineering deans have pledged to take specific concrete actions to broaden the participation of, and outcomes for, demographic populations underrepresented in engineering and STEM fields. In 1980, Slaughter was appointed by President Jimmy Carter to become director of the National Science Foundation (NSF). During his tenure, he implemented policies that supported programs designed to expand science and engineering education at historically Black colleges and universities (HBCUs). In 2015, the White House recognized his exceptional mentoring with the Presidential Award for Excellence in Science, Mathematics, and Engineering Mentoring. He also received the USC Provost Mentoring Award in 2016 and the USC Presidential Medallion—the university's highest distinction—in 2019. He is the 1987 Black Engineer of the Year.

David L. Steward

Dave Steward is chairman of World Wide Technology, Inc, an information technology and supply chain solution provider headquartered in St. Louis, MO. WWT now employs 1,381 people in 48 states and six countries—South Korea, Singapore, China, Germany, Brazil, and Mexico. Steward describes the company as "flexible, innovative, with an entrepreneurial spirit, and the ability to raise the bar in bringing technical solutions and value that go above and beyond." Steward is also co-author of *Doing Business by the Good Book: 52 Lessons on Success Straight from the Bible*. Steward and his company support the United Way, Variety Club, Boy Scouts of America, St. Patrick Center, Ronald McDonald House, Girls Inc., St. Louis Science Center, St. Louis Sports Commission, the YMCA, and his church. He is the 2012 Black Engineer of the Year.

Dr. Lydia Thomas

Dr. Lydia Thomas was honored as the 2003 Black Engineer of the Year at the 17th annual BEYA STEM Conference. She is a former president and CEO of Noblis, a nonprofit science, technology, and strategy organization. Prior to Noblis, Thomas was with The MITRE Corporation from 1973 to 1996. In 2002, Thomas was appointed by President George W. Bush to serve as founding member of the President's Homeland Security Advisory Council. In 2005 she was appointed co-chair of the Government University Industry Research Roundtable of the National Academies. Dr. Thomas is a member of the American Institute of Aeronautics and Astronautics; American Society of Toxicology; National Defense Industrial Association; the Teratology Society; and the International Women's Forum. She serves on the board of directors of the Cabot Corporation, Mueller Water Products, Inc., Washington Mutual Investors Fund, the United States Energy Association, the Northern Virginia Technology Council, the Conference Board, and is a member of the Charles Stark Draper Laboratory.

Dr. Calvin Mackie

Dr. Calvin Mackie, the recipient of the 2002 Black Engineer of the Year Award for College-level Education, runs a nonprofit organization to help serve families connected to the military. The New Orleans-based STEM NOLA promotes opportunities for people of color in the wind power, friction, rockets, and robotics industries. Born in New Orleans, Mackie graduated from the very first high school for Black Americans in the city. In 1990, he earned a bachelor's degree in mathematics from Morehouse College and a mechanical engineering degree from Georgia Tech through a dual-degree program. He also completed a master's degree and a Ph.D., both in mechanical engineering. Following graduation, Mackie joined the faculty at Tulane University, where he pursued research related to heat transfer, fluid dynamics, energy efficiency, and renewable energy.

H. RUSSELL FRISBY, JR.

FOREWARD

by H. Russell Frisby, Jr., Esq.

Fifty years ago, I was a senior in college taking some Black studies courses when I came across Samuel F. Yette's book, *The Choice: The Issue of Black Survival in America.* It set forth the proposition that, as a result of this country's move from an industrial society to a computer society, Blacks were becoming obsolete in the face of technological and scientific advancements. The book also emphasized the importance of taking immediate steps to ensure the Black community participated and understood the ramifications of the computer revolution. That was something that always stuck with me.

Fast-forward eight years. Discontented with my law practice, I spoke to a law school classmate who was the chief of staff to the chairman of the Federal Communications Commission. He suggested that if I wanted to do something exciting and impactful, I should join the Common Carrier Bureau of the FCC (now called the Wireline Competition Bureau). He argued that, while radio, TV, and cable were all the rage, the real future was in telecommunications, or telecom. I took him up on the offer, joined the FCC, and was immediately assigned to the Computer II Inquiry Task Force. In that proceeding, the primary question before the Commission was, "Should it regulate computers and computer communications?".

As the youngest lawyer on the task force, I ended up writing the core of what became the FCC's final decision in the Computer II Inquiry. In that decision the FCC made several landmark rulings that continue to shape telecommunications and the metaverse: It refused to regulate computers, deregulated enhanced computer (information) services, and also deregulated the provision of telephone and other telecommunications equipment. (At that point in time, you could only buy a telephone from the phone company.) We took these actions primarily for two reasons. First, we believed that regulation would only thwart technological innovation. Second, we thought regulation would either delay or prevent the development of the evolving information pipeline (which we now call the internet). Ironically, the FCC was prodded in part by two young congressmen. One was Ed Markey, who is now a senator from Massachusetts, and the second was a young congressman from Tennessee, Al Gore. They were very instrumental in persuading the FCC to act.

A year later, I left the Bureau and worked for FCC Commissioner, Joe Fogarty. With Fogarty's help, a group of us convinced then-FCC Commissioner Tyrone Brown that the FCC should undertake an effort to get Black people involved in telecom, similar to its ongoing efforts in the areas of broadcast and cable. We held a two-day conference with Congressman Parren Mitchell, the leader on minority business issues, as the keynote speaker. The conference focused on opportunities in the long-distance resale and cellular markets because the barriers to entry were low at that point—everyone was on equal footing starting at ground zero. The conference was well attended by Blacks and whites, males and females. Unfortunately, for the most part, Blacks never followed through afterwards. Many of the white attendees and elsewhere did, though, and they formed competitive local exchange carriers, or CLECs. Many of these individuals became millionaires. The CLECs drove innovation as well as lower-price services in the telecom market that benefited everyone. They even forced the local Bell Telephone companies to compete for the first time in 100 years. Unfortunately, the wealth and jobs generated by CLECs did not flow down to the Black community.

Moving ahead 15 years or so, I stepped down as the first Black chair of the Maryland Public Service Commission, a role I held for three years, to become the president of the Competitive Telecom Association, also known as Comptel. Although our major members were AT&T and MCI (before they were acquired by SBC and Verizon), our membership included hundreds of CLECs. In that role I came to know a number of CEOs and senior management quite well. For the most part they were decent people with good business minds, but they were by no means geniuses. Many of them did not start out in telecom. But, they saw an opportunity when the barriers were low, and they had the foresight to move forward on it. Unfortunately, and all too often, I was the only person of color in the room. There were also very few women in those spaces. By the late 1990s, the barriers of entry were sadly too high for anyone who had not been there from the early stages to get involved.

I wonder what would have happened had we, meaning Blacks and other minorities, been there in the beginning of the telecommunications revolution, which is entering a new phase with the development of the metaverse. I doubt that we would be talking as much about a digital divide. Likewise, I doubt that we would just now be coming to the realization that our children must get into STEM and STEAM programs if they are to keep up and survive. These are the important issues Dr. Taborn addresses in "Metaquake," and it is precisely why this book is such a profoundly important read as we gaze at the beginnings of the metaverse. Fifty years after the transition from an industrial society to a digital society, we are asking the same question: "What do we have to do to ensure Blacks and other minorities survive and thrive in the face of rapid technological change?".

I strongly agree with Dr. Taborn that Blacks have been traditionally left behind in the digital revolution. It is imperative that minorities stake a presence now. If we are not there at the beginning of this new phase, we won't be there at all, and we will become the obsolete population that Samuel Yette described.

"Metaquake" is a must-read that not only offers keen insight into needed strategies for a strong minority presence in the metaverse market, but it also offers sound solutions for continued engagement. Dr. Taborn is raising a call to arms, and we all must respond *swiftly*.

TABLE OF CONTENTS

CHAPTER ONE:
What Is the Metaverse Era?

"Technology is best when it brings people together."
— *Matt Mullenweg, Founder of WordPress*

A change is coming. It is a game-changer called the Metaverse Era, and it will rock us like an earthquake. There is a funny thing about change; it is often slow and unnoticed until the results are apparent. Look at how long it took us to recognize climate change or the impact of smoking on our health. Despite scientific warnings, it took an overwhelming body of evidence before we saw what had always been right in front of us. The coming Metaquake is a dramatic change that won't take decades or even years. The Metaquake is happening right now. The only question is are we prepared for it, or will we be overtaken and left behind?

So, why does it take us so long to recognize when change happens? Most of us live in the moment; we are quick to forget the past and its lessons and can't wrap our heads around tomorrow. The coming Metaquake is even more complex because to comprehend tomorrow's endless possibilities we need to understand the past that has created where we are today. The metaverse of tomorrow is here right now.

Underrepresented communities in the workforce do not have the luxury of memory lapses. When competing for jobs, building a business, or getting training and education, the stakes are too high. The new Meta Era we have stepped into redefines how we work, play, and socialize. It's creating new companies using innovative technologies such as artificial intelligence (AI), virtual reality (VR), and augmented reality (AR). We see applications in every industry harnessing the power of cloud computing, from healthcare to education and gaming to manufacturing.

This next wave of societal innovation is advancing faster than any change we have experienced globally. Over time, the World Wide Web has moved from having data and content held by only the big technology companies (Web 2.0) to a decentralized web (Web 3.0). Although the winners and losers have yet to be chosen, this is precisely the stage of change where people of color have always missed out. The question at hand is whether underrepresented communities will seize the opportunities of the Meta Era or allow prevailing circumstances to relegate them to a consumer class.

We are going through a fundamental change in the world. We're not simply trying to bridge the digital divide by deploying technology that could level the playing field for underserved communities. It is estimated that less than 3 percent of data scientists are Black, and less than 15 percent are women. And yet data science is one of the most transformational careers of all time. As we look at Web 3.0 and the metaverse, the use of blockchain for peer-to-peer security, non-fungible tokens for digital ownership, and digital currencies for revenue, these technologies represent an opportunity to shift from consumption to creation. Web 3.0 as the infrastructure and the metaverse as a persistent digital environment have the potential to reset how individuals of color engage as participants in the next-gen internet.

Opportunities for Growth in the Meta Era

In just a few decades, so much radical change has taken place. In the past, just one technological advancement would define an entire generation. But the last 30 years have seen many technological revolutions simultaneously. We went from computers that took up the size of a house to portable ones that could be on your desk to ones that you could hold in your hands. These technology growth cycles have developed in stages that often overlap. The steps are research, technology transfer to innovators and creators, products to the marketplace, and consumer acceptance.

The metaverse is still mainly in the stage of creation and innovation. This stage is ideal for opportunities because, as Meta CEO Mark

Zuckerberg has said, "The metaverse will not be created by one company. It will be built by creators and developers making new experiences and digital items that are interoperable and unlock a massively larger creative economy than the one constrained by today's platforms and policies." But suppose the Meta Era is playing out the same way as other technology growth cycles. In that case, people of color need to catch up in developing technology-driven businesses, job training, education, and entertainment in the metaverse.

To succeed in the Meta Era requires an understanding of our analog-to-digital past. In the technology chapter of *The Covenant with Black America,* I observed that in each successive wave of industry innovation, "Companies were created, lifestyles changed, and fortunes made and lost. Ironically, when these windows of opportunity opened, Black people could not exploit them. Black people were shut out at the birth of digital technologies when the most wealth was created. When they came in, they participated as consumers."

The good news is that the Meta Era is not entirely new. People of color have been involved at some level in every technology development cycle, all the way back to the "punch card (used for automatic tabulation in the 1890 census), the calculation and printing of the first Social Security checks in the 1930s, and the introduction of the PC to a mass audience in the 1980s" *(IBM: The Rise and Fall and Reinvention of a Global Icon,* by James W. Cortada, a history of one of the most influential American companies of the last century). Web 1.0 was ushered in partially by Black IBM innovator Dr. Mark Dean, who holds three of the seven original patents on the IBM personal computer. Because of Dean's contributions, technology titans like Bill Gates and Michael Dell launched startups, which led to one of the most significant redistributions of wealth the world had ever seen. During this transformational stage, Black people were still engaged in fundamental civil rights and public accommodations challenges. While Black people were making tremendous individual contributions to technology, little innovation was happening at the community level. That would later lead to a widening of the economic gap.

Closing the Digital Divide

The digital divide has long existed. According to Larry Irving, a former administrator of the National Telecommunications and Information Administration in the U.S. Department of Commerce, the "digital divide" is between those with access to new technologies and those without. In a 1998 report called "Falling Through the Net: Defining the Digital Divide," Irving said the digital divide is one of America's leading economic and civil rights issues. Part I of the report surveyed household access to telephones, computers, and the internet, updating the surveys in two previous reports: "Falling Through the Net: A Survey of the 'Have Nots' in Rural and Urban America" (July 1995) and "Falling Through the Net II: New Data on the Digital Divide" (July 1998). The NTIA found that although more households are connected, certain households are gaining access to new technologies far more quickly, while others are falling further behind.

In the global digital divide, poor and low-income communities worldwide have faced an uphill battle since the Second World War to get into the game and play a role other than as workers or consumers of technology. We need those communities to be able to use science and technology to build wealth.

The good news is that the metaverse has the potential to move all of us beyond this intractable divide. Metaverse technologies allow decentralization of the web. Decentralizing technologies will result in a reset, and big technology companies will be less relevant. Rather than giving all your information to a social media company, you will own and control your digital avatar and creativity, giving you more agency over your data. While the digital divide is primarily focused on access to hardware, broadband, and content, the metaverse's decentralized model is an opportunity for the redistribution of knowledge between the haves and have-nots. The metaverse is a significant transformation in how the world will use technology and how technology will be organized. It is an opportunity for people of color that cannot be underestimated.

Imagine the potential of a combined federally funded research center for historically Black colleges and universities (HBCUs). I promoted this concept in 2006 to help HBCUs compete for research dollars. In 2020, federally funded R&D at universities increased 3.7 percent to $46.2 billion. For many reasons, HBCUs received less than 2 percent of that budget. Adding to HBCUs' underfunding woes is that their endowments are already typically much less than those of Ivy League institutions. Not one HBCU has an endowment of over $1 billion; Harvard, by comparison, has an endowment of almost $55 billion. However, the metaverse is an opportunity to close this gap. A federally funded research center is possible since the metaverse already has the infrastructure to facilitate real-time collaboration among top HBCU researchers and students. This setting could reduce the high cost of new building construction, and HBCUs could pool their existing resources accessible in the metaverse. For HBCUs, the metaverse could finally be the path to a more equitable outcome in the federal research distribution challenge. User interactive security protocols would protect the intellectual properties of each university, making trust issues less of a concern.

That concept of bridging the digital divide—using technology to advance opportunities for people underrepresented in STEM careers—is part of what is built into the metaverse's core value. The Meta Era can be different from the previous four revolutionary technology advancements that we have seen over seven decades. From industrial automation to personal computers, networking, and social media in the digital age, these past revolutions defined winners and losers at every stage. From the beginning, it was a stacked deck against people of color. The world is now facing another technology earthquake, and we need to recognize that the metaverse is an opportunity to even that playing field forever.

Change Through Global Crisis

It is crucial to keep in mind that the metaverse wouldn't have taken root as quickly as it did if not for the COVID-19 pandemic. While the metaverse's foundational technology has existed for a while, its development accelerated because of the waves of lockdowns in 2020. We already had augmented and virtual reality computing technologies in place, which people were using in some form. And, of course, all of us had cellphones. Video technology has been around since *Dick Tracy*. But after the pandemic, most cellphone users embraced these applications out of necessity. There were more opportunities for telehealth because of government regulations. More doctors were able to deliver services through video technology, with insurance companies ready to pay the bill. The use of video brought together over 30 million people under this digital sky. Before 2020, most of us would have screamed if our bosses had made us turn on our cameras during an online seminar. That sentiment has changed. More people are comfortable being on camera all the time for work, in Zoom meetings for family gatherings, and as patients interacting with doctors remotely in telehealth exchanges.

The Health Resources and Services Administration defines telehealth as electronic information and telecommunications technologies to support and promote long-distance clinical health care, patient and professional health-related education, and public health and health administration. The use of telehealth services surged during the COVID-19 pandemic. A 2020 study found telehealth use during the initial COVID-19 peak (March to April 2020) increased from less than 1 percent of visits to as many as 80 percent in places with high pandemic prevalence. Digital interaction was becoming the dominant form of communication—an important step toward the public's embracing of the metaverse and its interactivity model.

The pandemic also impacted government regulations, aiding the acceleration of the metaverse's development. While technology growth spurred by pandemic necessity has opened more opportunities for engagement, we need to understand the next step of navigating this new environment—bringing us to the metaverse and its basic landscape. We know it can be 2D (or 3D with total immersion and glasses on), but beyond those simple elements, what exactly is the metaverse?

Decentralization in the Metaverse

Dr. Louis Rosenberg, who developed the first functional AR system at the Air Force Research Laboratory, defines the metaverse as a *persistent* and immersive simulated world experienced in the first person by large groups of simultaneous users who share a strong sense of mutual presence. One of the critical components of Rosenberg's definition is the notion of multiple simultaneous users.

Picture this: You are sitting in a movie theatre and looking at the screen—a stagnant experience. That is the internet. If you get up and step into the movie, that's VR. If the people in the theater can go into the movie with you at the same time, and you all have agency over yourself and make the movie, that's the metaverse. You are creating an extended reality so that everything that exists in the physical world is now part of a digital twin, and you can create in the metaverse what exists in the physical world—which is why we use the term "twin" here. Thus, there are tons of new opportunities, with no physical limitations. Whether it's 2D or engaging in an environment with a headset, it's the same because the mind interprets it the same way.

The metaverse takes visual and audio technology and puts it all together. Think again about watching that movie live in a theater. The screen story is coming right at you. You sit there as you take in the story and are aware of your surroundings; you're eating popcorn, surrounded by images and sound. Now, imagine once more that you get up and go into the movie, but you're alone in the existing story. You're in 3D, virtual reality. But the minute the others join you and interact together with autonomy, it becomes much more—the metaverse.

You might hear some people refer to the metaverse as "Web 3.0," but Web 3.0, as you know, is just linking together a bunch of systems and computers. The metaverse builds communities and nations—unlike the internet, which creates only narrow cast areas. We will talk about why that's possible and why the metaverse cannot exist without the concept of the blockchain technology behind it. That's where the opportunities truly come in for many of our companies.

The metaverse also allows people to own something. Ownership is the game-changer we've been waiting for. Are we up to it? God brought me this far to tell the story to draw attention to the things plaguing our nation right now—capital in too few hands, wealth in too few hands.

This is an opportunity for the American dream we all believed in: that we all can have a part of something that makes everybody whole.

One of the key reasons this change is possible is because blockchain and other new technological developments allow for decentralization, which fosters a more democratic distribution of resources available in the metaverse. More opportunities, more choices.

Choice is key. Why would I buy a pair of tennis shoes for only $29 while other people buy tennis shoes for $300, $400, or $600? Because tennis shoes don't matter to me. So, tennis shoes are not a need; they are a want. As more people go into these metaverses (there will be many metaverses, and they may never talk to each other), you will have the chance to walk into many specialized areas.

You're going to look at pictures and see a house. You'll say, "I want that house," but you'll have to pay for it. And that's where the non-fungible tokens (NFT) market will explode. The economic infrastructure is critical. We're working with banks now to do that because, just like the tennis shoes, it's all about choice. It's either a need or a want. If it's a "want," people will pay for it. The metaverse is needed for access to the things people will want.

Another area where the metaverse will make a big difference involves workforces like our farming communities. Imagine local family farms that have fresh crops ready for market. The farmers don't necessarily have access to selling to their markets, so they sell their products to a company that doesn't do the farming but is buying crops from every other farmer and not giving them a competitive price. Imagine if, instead, these farmers created a marketplace for selling their products through this metaverse. Now, there are some other issues we can argue about, like how they export them, but the fundamental concept is the same. If the metaverse has already created a like-minded community, they would know, or a farmer would see, a group of farmers in STEM City USA. They don't have to search the country for that market. We've already created a community for them in STEM City, and they can instantly reach that community with a click of a button.

Let's now come back to this thing called a blockchain. If I want to send somebody money, I don't have to go through Visa or MasterCard. I don't have to go through a centralized bank. Blockchain decentralizes information, tracking transactions through a secured ledger on a peer-to-peer network. I can cut out the expensive third parties to process transactions and save money from that cost for myself. Because through the blockchain, you get all these currencies popping up without the need for a trusted third party, which allows you to create new value in the digital space. For example, you can buy music. You can purchase goods and services. You can bring a lot of things online. Anybody can do it without needing major institutions to help them create their business in this area. Because it's all decentralized, you have an opportunity for millions of people to play in that world.

Imagine you're looking at a picture behind me right now. You could buy that with a bitcoin; that could be an NFT, and the only argument is who wants to pay for it. Remember, people spend a lot of money to advertise on Facebook. That's all digital. So, if you stop and think about it, there's a lot of value in the digital world that takes place all the time.

The metaverse is built on the blockchain NFTs, and that's where we're going in the future. If anyone reading this cares for a young person, make sure you point them toward courses like Unity and Unity programming. Start looking at all the software used to build the metaverse and other places. They will be critical, and they will pay off a lot.

The future is bright for a global society moving into the metaverse, but history shows us there will be cracks in the system. The main thing we all must remember, though, is that the time to act is right now before this opportunity passes us by.

DR. MELVIN GREER

DIXIE GARR

CHAPTER TWO:
The Birth of the Metaverse

"When the metaverse was born, very few Blacks were on the scene."

The year 1959 changed the world forever. That was the year pioneering engineers introduced the microchip. Almost immediately, technology had capabilities unimaginable a few years earlier. Computers that once occupied entire buildings would soon be small enough to sit on a desk and, later, in the palm of your hand. Because of powerful microprocessors, computer modeling and simulations that previously took months could now happen in hours, and this jump in technology was all because of the microchip. It ushered in the digital age and laid the groundwork for today's metaverse, a virtual world that will become increasingly important in our society. Without microchips, there would be no way to store the vast amount of data that makes up the metaverse. Microchips are essential for providing the processing power needed to render computer graphics.

At the beginning of this "new era in integrated electronics," when fortunes were being amassed and industries redefined, Black people were relegated to the sidelines. At the time, only one HBCU had an accredited engineering program: Howard University. It would be years before a coalition of industry leaders, private foundations, and educators from HBCUs succeeded in expanding opportunities for minorities in engineering and computer science programs housed at HBCU campuses. With all the power the microchip released, the personalization of computing power was the next building block.

History and Impact of the Microchip

In 2014, the City of Dallas proclaimed September 12 as Jack Kilby Day, and Texas Instruments (TI) celebrated the inventor by sharing the story of his creation to inspire students everywhere. According to TI, technology changed forever on Sept. 12, 1958. That was the day Kilby, a young TI engineer, invented the integrated circuit, which ushered in the era of modern electronics.

Kilby's career began after the Second World War, when he served as a radio operator. He received his Bachelor of Science degree in electrical engineering in 1947, and he began his career with an electronic components manufacturer focused on developing circuits for consumer electronic products. Kilby joined Dallas-based TI in June 1958.

During the summer of 2019, the Department of Electrical and Computer Engineering (ECE) at the University of Illinois Urbana-Champaign said Kilby's integrated circuit helped make the historic Apollo 11 mission possible. The components in the electronic circuit were fabricated in a single piece of semiconductor material half the size of a paper clip. Before this integration, the single parts had to be connected using small wires, limiting large-scale production. Kilby's innovation launched a technological revolution.

"The integrated circuit made it possible to realize complicated functions in a small area," said Naresh R. Shanbhag, the ECE Illinois Jack S. Kilby Professor of Electrical and Computer Engineering. "They replaced vacuum tubes—bulky, power-hungry, and unreliable." Shanbhag believes that the most fantastic part of this story is that in 1969, just a few years later, the integrated circuit was used to help us "journey to the moon and back."

The microchip laid the conceptual and technical foundation for the entire field of modern microelectronics, which made personal computers, cellphones, hand-held calculators, and portable GPS systems possible in today's information age.

In October 2000, Kilby won the Nobel Prize in Physics. His Nobel citation recognized him for his invention of the integrated circuit and its impact on communications, the computer industry, medical science, radar, and entertainment. Kilby also co-invented the pocket calculator during an extensive career at TI before retiring in 1983.

In an interview published in the *Electronic Engineering Times,* Kilby said that he was shocked but pleased to win a share of the Nobel Prize in physics for his contribution to the computer revolution. Kilby did not take all the credit for launching the information age. He acknowledged that many people and contributions had gone into its development. He later told reporters that he had been surprised at the range of electronic and digital devices that flowed from the integrated circuit over the decades since its invention. "Certainly, we're in for more of the same for some time," he said. "Electronics will continue to get cheaper, and new applications will come along, which I don't think I've visualized very well." His daughter told KERA News for North Texas that she believed "his favorite invention was the chip—simply because it was useful."

Independently of one another, in 1959, Kilby and Robert Noyce showed that many transistors, resistors, and capacitors could be grouped on a single board of semiconductor material. In 2014, the *New York Times* noted that "Mr. Kilby and Dr. Noyce, then with Fairchild Semiconductor, were named as inventors in their companies' applications for patents for the integrated circuit. After years of legal battles, Fairchild and Texas Instruments decided to cross-license their technologies, creating a world information industries market worth more than $1 trillion annually." The integrated circuit, or microchip, was a turning point for computers and a turning point for an entire technology industry. Without it, of course, today's metaverse would not be possible.

Early Black Tech Pioneers Who Helped Pave the Way

The lack of access to engineering education and computer science careers for Black people during the dawn of the microchip era was profound. It wasn't until 1988 that Texas Instruments appointed software engineer Dixie Garr as a director for its systems group. Garr made history by becoming the first level 3 director at Texas Instruments. Garr graduated from Grambling State University summa cum laude in 1975. It was a troubled era when many Americans believed they could no longer compete in manufacturing. Garr did graduate work at UCLA as a Hughes Aircraft fellow in engineering and computer science before moving to TI in 1981, where she worked for almost 20 years.

With newly invented semiconductor devices, process control brought the United States back into the game, and Garr was one of the bright stars who made it happen. In one of her seminal papers, Garr and a co-author laid out a development environment encompassing control methodologies, showing it was possible with careful protection of memory, input-output resources, multiprocessors, and real-time databases.

In 1997, Garr won the Black Engineer of the Year Award for Professional Achievement in Industry. After attending the Stanford University Executive Program, Garr led engineering teams at TI, working on programs in defense and communications before joining Cisco Systems.

Other Black pioneers include Art George, senior vice president and manager of analog engineering operations at TI. During Black History Month in 2013, George gave a presentation on the evolution of the integrated circuit industry. George's team is responsible for providing engineering support and driving down production costs across TI's analog product portfolio. George brought to the role unique insight gained through various operational positions, where he was involved in developing thousands of new integrated circuit products. He received a Bachelor of Science degree in electrical engineering from Southern University in Baton Rouge, LA, and a master's in engineering management from Southern Methodist University in Dallas, TX. In 2007, George was honored at the Black Engineer of the Year Awards conference as a member of the 100 Most Important Blacks in Technology and career achievement honoree. Both awards are sponsored by *U.S. Black Engineer* magazine and the Council of the Engineering Deans of the Historically Black Colleges and Universities.

Another pioneer is Dr. Melvin Greer, who made history as the chief data scientist at Intel. His primary job is developing and adopting AI technologies, an important component of the metaverse's future. Greer was born in Detroit, MI. His mother was on the staff of every school he attended in Detroit until college, so he would ride with her every day from home to school. She used that time to teach him valuable life lessons. He also had great teachers at Miller High School, which at the time was the only high school Black people could attend in Detroit.

Greer's career would take him around the world. One of Greer's first jobs was at the General Motors Tech Center, working on artificial intelligence precursors. After graduating from college, he spent time as a chief financial officer in Germany, France, and England. Then he served as a chief information officer in Hong Kong, followed by four years in Brazil and one in Canada. When he moved back to the United States, Greer worked for Lockheed Martin.

Later, at Intel, his research helped access a deeper understanding of artificial intelligence. His job was to figure out how to take AI capabilities and turn them into remarkable things in data science. Such work involves all the technical knowledge you would expect. Still, it also requires an understanding of AI's impact on social change, including its impact on underserved communities and people of color. The ethical, responsible use of AI is a critical component of the work Greer and his team continue to do to understand and ensure that what they build doesn't fall prey to unintended consequences. Greer is also an award winner at the Black Engineer of the Year Awards.

Greer's professional experience gives him a unique understanding of the metaverse. Because of this, it's very useful to hear firsthand what he has to say. Greer feels that the metaverse is important "because of the convergence of technologies or building blocks, which changes the reality we experience." He says, "It's more immersive. It's interconnected. It's virtual. When we look at these new technologies—augmented reality, artificial intelligence, blockchain, and cryptocurrencies—they have the potential to redefine how we work, socialize, and learn."

Greer feels that the internet is going through "a considerable transformation." He believes that interest in the concept of the metaverse is "fueling a whole number of really important predictions, things like by 2030, we may be spending more time in the metaverse than we spend in the real world, and people are going to be applying for jobs, earning a living, meeting with friends and shopping, even getting married, using virtual capacity that's in the metaverse."

Greer offers a current example from the business world as proof: "KPMG announced they started holding workplace meetings in the metaverse, including collaborative conversations—some around business and some the water cooler type. They were conversations between virtual people in the metaverse and real-world team members on screens. They were able to do white boarding and have interactive discussions. It created a complete social presence."

Greer looks to the future and notes that "in the next 10 years, it's predicted that we'll see higher education delivered in the metaverse. It will transform the concepts of music, fashion, and concerts. Businesses and governments also are going to completely reshape the way they do business and collaborate because they will have the power and reach of the metaverse to get to anyone, anywhere, at any time, globally, so it's going to be exciting."

When most people think of the metaverse, they may think about gaming, entertainment, and escaping reality. None of this would've been possible without Greer's work. His view on the industry overall and how we finally arrived here is valuable, but he also stresses the importance for people of color to be aware of these upcoming opportunities, especially those piloted by STEM City USA.

"First, let me say that STEM City USA is cutting edge. It actively represents what the future holds in a metaverse environment. But this idea of immersion and a virtual world is not altogether new. When we look at immersive storytelling in spoken word, text, and movies, these are all parts of the roadmap of the metaverse concept, where we create an immersive world that's not real. And now, we're bending physics to create virtual environments that augment this concept that we've been building on from the beginning of time. This evolution from Web 2.0 to Web 3.0 distributed web technologies is at the core of this inflection point that we're talking about, which is the metaverse."

Greer notes that this is a special time in history because of the convergence of many technologies. "Each of the technical building blocks—virtual and augmented reality, artificial intelligence, blockchain, and cryptocurrencies—each of these emerging technologies has been maturing at its own individual rate. What's happening now is they're converging into a new set of capabilities that can be collaborative and are currently creating this idea of a metaverse. Each of them fills gaps and accelerates technologies and the technology adoption of the other ones, so we see huge investments in technological advancements around virtual environments. Facebook, now called Meta, is putting $10 billion into metaverse technologies. Microsoft has invested $69 billion in Activision Blizzard, this multiplayer game. They believe the metaverse will change how we will operate and interact. And these companies are looking to ensure that they help set the stage for how the metaverse rolls out and how we will participate. And they want to be in the best position to help monetize it and learn from the data it collects. So, the industry is not singular. A broad network or ecosystem of technical capabilities is coming together to form the metaverse."

Greer believes that key elements "have been brought together to make all this possible, and they involve this idea of computing, memory, and storage. We continue to see the evolution of Moore's Law and the computational growth that's being made available, propelling this idea of being able to create virtual worlds." Moore's Law refers to an observation made in 1965 by Gordon Moore, a founder of Intel, that the number of transistors on a microchip will double every year while its cost is cut in half during the same time frame. In general, this means that the capabilities of our computers will continue to increase while costing less with each improvement. In many ways, the phrase has become shorthand in the tech industry for exponential growth.

Greer adds, "Cloud computing is the other essential thing, just as foundational as computing, memory, and storage. The reason cloud is so foundational is that we wouldn't have easy access to or the aggregate power of larger and larger data sets without cloud computing. And these more extensive data sets allow us to start understanding how we can manipulate physics, space and time, and represent avatars and physical and virtual worlds using the computing power that is helping the metaverse become a reality."

Greer also notes the role that quantum computing will play in the next level. Right now, "We're seeing advances in the core hardware, which is essential. Next-generation hardware and infrastructure will be brain-inspired so that neuromorphic computing will move us beyond traditional computing. And even as we move into quantum and quantum capabilities, we'll see that infrastructure grow. But correspondingly, we see the desire to move into more considerable abilities to understand, aggregate, and analyze data, because it's this data, especially the information that's in the cloud, that is allowing us to provide the analytics, the artificial intelligence, the data science that makes it possible to create these advanced virtual worlds."

One thing to bear in mind, Greer explains, is that we are in a transition.

"The shift is from Web 2.0—where we have several companies taking advantage of users' data to generate larger and larger revenue streams—to Web 3.0 technologies, where the idea of data sovereignty is built into the system." This is where "we move away from users presenting data to others to creators who are maximizing the use of their imaginations and creative capabilities to monetize those in a cryptocurrency blockchain environment."

It is also important to understand why the metaverse offers more opportunity. Greer explains that the "decentralization of web technologies, the sovereignty of the data we create and own, and democratization of the compensation models are driven by individual creations. One of the first steps in developing distributed compensation is the idea of non-fungible tokens. We're seeing creators using NFTs inside this Web 3.0 decentralized infrastructure capability. Along with blockchain and crypto, these creators take full advantage of their data sovereignty, security, and monetization opportunities."

To take full advantage of this opportunity will require some effort, though. Greer says that "unfortunately, having this capacity does not translate into our ability to do so without some education. We need to be very clear-eyed about what will be required for all citizens to be able to take advantage of these new environments. I'm excited about this because young people are most engaged in this activity."

When Greer considers specific opportunities for people of color in metaverse development, he notes that it goes back to the youth and how they are early adopters of technological change and trends. "My sons are 11 and 13, and they've been working on Roblox and Minecraft, which have the same construct as distributed web technologies. So, when they get their allowance, they buy Minecraft coins that allow them to create virtual environments that provide them access to new tools. They can develop those modules for themselves, which become revenue streams they can also monetize. So, what's exciting about it is, not only do we have a marriage of the capability, but we now have an education or a roadmap that engages young people and young people of color so they can become interested parties and active participants in all three phases of the creation, distribution, and monetization."

Monetization is a key element as we look at the potential metaverse economy overall. Greer has had a front row seat to such developments. He feels that "big businesses and governments see the potential of this new economy, where they have direct access to the creators. They will be in the form of changing their business model." He points out that STEM City USA will play an important role because of the new STEM City coin, which he says "is a crucial step toward a deeper and richer understanding of how people of color can engage in an economic and business trade mechanism without having to be bound by larger forces like banking, or a big company that may drive a wedge between the creator and the people who are trying to provide an excellent service to them. And so, this new coin that is part of STEM City is the most exciting thing. I can't wait to see how people react to it."

As to where computing power will take the metaverse overall, he says that tech has already "hinted a bit at the move from traditional computing, application-specific integrated circuits tuned and optimized for specific applications, to new kinds of computing models like neuromorphic computing, which is brain-inspired. The potential of neuromorphic computing is critical because when it comes to creating the metaverse, we have to consider the impact on energy consumption and sustainability. But as we move to neuromorphic computing, where we have one-tenth of 1 percent of the energy consumption in traditional computing, it will allow for an immediate and rapid expansion of computing in these virtual environments and quantum in the future."

So, where can we get started? According to Greer, there are a couple of essential things to bear in mind. "First, it's important to understand the basic building blocks associated with the metaverse. We have already discussed some of them: AR, VR applications, artificial intelligence, blockchain, and cryptocurrency. Understanding these technologies is the very first step to figuring out how these building blocks come together and converge to create this thing we call the metaverse. I'd suggest investigations start with understanding smart contracts, using virtual worlds in fashion and music, or even using OpenSea and building an NFT."

He emphasizes it is more than just getting educated. "Finding a great mentor and coach is the most significant impact on career advancement. As a data scientist who mentors and coaches several people, I know this is a number one determinant for career success. Athletes already know this, which is why people like LeBron James have 13 or 14 coaches to help them become very good at maximizing their potential."

It's a special time with rare opportunities available. Greer believes this is "because the barrier to getting hands-on experience with these tools is so low. Now is the time to get a hands-on understanding of how they work. It's important to understand how these technologies converge and what they mean. Get to know OpenSea, the largest marketplace for crypto collectibles. Understand how bitcoin development operates in STEM City and figure out why it's so important and what we can do with it. Getting a hands-on understanding of these technologies, finding a great mentor and coach, and understanding the building blocks as they converge would be great first steps I would ask someone to take if they're looking to take advantage of the future of the metaverse."

Beyond individual opportunities for jobs, Greer also offers some insight about greater business opportunities. "Whether you're a small business or a large business, there are some critical elements that you want to start focusing on. First, start looking for tangible outcomes. Don't go into it with the technology driving the conversation. Make sure that what you're trying to achieve is tied to actual business outcomes. Use some real established KPIs and let the business drive what you do. Start small. Consider the idea of partnerships and being able to bring together partners that can help deflect some of the risks associated with adoption."

Greer adds that he "can't overestimate or overstate the importance of developing a data strategy. Understanding how data impacts small, medium, and large businesses and how that data can be used to provide insight, make better business decisions, and drive growth is a crucial step in understanding what this metaverse conversation is all about. You don't need to create a Bitcoin; you don't need to buy cryptocurrency. You don't need to have a blockchain implementation. You need to understand data and data strategies around management and governance, security, and non-technical issues like ethical and responsible use of data."

With this in mind, metaverse analytics will open doors for new business pipelines. "I'm a data scientist. I'm always focused on AI. My primary job is the development and adoption of AI technologies. And artificial intelligence, as it matures, will become part of a solution-focused ecosystem. And so, analytics, present-generation AI, and even next-generation AI will be required by metaverse creators. This includes the data sovereignty component and the zero-trust capabilities necessary for adoption. The future of the metaverse is not built just inside AI; it is horizontal. So, the growth and future of the metaverse involve the horizontal maturity of AI, AR, VR, blockchain, and crypto technologies. These technologies will create the infrastructure that will be harnessed to build this virtual metaverse environment. Because no single technology will rule the day, analytics is important, but all these other ones are, too. And, of course, there are some we haven't even thought of that will be coming online. They're going to be important, too. But analytics is an important one to start with."

Overall, Greer believes that success in the metaverse involves "developing an entrepreneurial mindset." He says this is critical because "each of these fields revolves around understanding, using, and analyzing data. That's why being able to drive business growth is directly related to understanding how to ingest, analyze, and gain insight from data. Some companies sound like one thing but are, in fact, a very different thing. A company provides personalized attire and clothing for men, women, and children. This company sounds like it's selling you clothes. But the company has very little to do with marketing clothes to you. It's about harnessing the power of the data associated with the algorithm that picks the clothes for you. And that algorithm is monetizing and driving business growth for the company. When we look at companies manufacturing cars, the best cars and trucks, and vehicles in the world, they are being built using data from users to improve their products. So, my advice to entrepreneurs is to harness the power of data, no matter your business."

TAKEAWAYS
CHAPTER TWO

- THE MICROCHIP LAID THE FOUNDATION FOR THE FIELD OF MICROELECTRONICS.

- BLACK PIONEERS LIKE DIXIE GARR, ART GEORGE, AND MELVIN GREER HELPED PAVE THE WAY.

- BY 2030, PEOPLE WILL BE APPLYING FOR JOBS, EARNING A LIVING, MEETING WITH FRIENDS, AND SHOPPING USING VIRTUAL CAPACITY IN THE METAVERSE.

- UNDERSTAND THE BASIC BUILDING BLOCKS ASSOCIATED WITH THE METAVERSE: AUGMENTED REALITY (AR), VIRTUAL REALITY (VR), ARTIFICIAL INTELLIGENCE (AI), BLOCKCHAIN, AND CRYPTOCURRENCY.

- UNDERSTAND HOW DATA IMPACTS SMALL, MEDIUM, AND LARGE BUSINESSES AND HOW THAT DATA CAN BE USED TO PROVIDE INSIGHT. METAVERSE CREATORS WILL REQUIRE NEXT-GENERATION AI.

DR. MARK DEAN

CHAPTER THREE:
The Personalization of Technology

Freedom is one thing; equality was something different.

As important as the microchip was as our first step toward the Meta Era, it was the personalization of technology that brought the benefits of computers to the masses. One of the key individuals in making that happen was Dr. Mark Dean, a man often recognized as the architect of the modern-day personal computer. Almost everything in your life has been affected by the work of Mark Dean. He developed the bus system, and the bus system brought large computers—the kind that used to need an entire room to operate—into desktop form. Dean holds three of the original nine patents that all PCs are based upon. Millions of jobs in information technology can be directly traced back directly to his work. In 2000, Dean was honored as the Black Engineer of the Year.

Dean has a unique perspective as a visionary engineer to speak about the role of the personal computer, its own development history, and how that history connects to the dawn of the metaverse. Think about how unique it is to hear the architect of the PC reflect on the potential advantages of the metaverse. His perspective takes us back to the very start—IBM.

Pioneering the Virtualization of Society

"The opportunity I had to work in an environment at IBM allowed us to build something that was new and inventive. It turned out to be a key tool in the advancement and support of everything from business, to communications, to entertainment and everything in between. We developed a system called IBM PC, which basically included technology that allowed people to do things more efficiently. The biggest contribution I made was primarily in the development of what was called the ISA bus. The ISA bus allowed people to connect different types of devices together, including fax machines and printers, and more memory, and displays, and video cards—essentially letting you expand the computer system. It basically defined PC compatibility back in the day. Most of the patents that I hold, including those three of the original nine for the original IBM PC, were in support of this ISA bus. I've done a lot of things since then obviously, but if I had to pick one contribution, that was probably the biggest contribution that I made. We were surprised that particular interface lasted so long. It probably lasted 15 years, which is a long time in technology terms. People used that particular bus for a long, long time, and we're pretty proud of its impact."

Dean notes that the original goal of the project at IBM was to move technology to the next level, past the analog machines of the day. "Originally, we developed that primarily to improve productivity for a person to get things done. The primary goal was to replace a typewriter with something that would allow me to edit it and print it out once, versus what we used to have to do with the typewriter. Beyond that, we wanted an electronic ledger or a spreadsheet so that we could perform calculations more efficiently than writing things down on a piece of paper and keeping ledgers manually, correcting them with pencils and erasers. We also wanted to build something to allow users to actually be an artist, to draw and create things, either architectural drawings, or diagrams or anything like that using electronic means versus using a piece of paper."

Dean was surprised by the impact. "This was 1981; productivity was measured at a different level. We thought we'd build maybe 200,000 systems in its lifetime and then go off and do something else. We didn't think that we were changing the world; we thought it'd be a useful tool. Little did we know that everybody wanted one. Companies all wanted to opt in and build similar systems, compatible systems, and add-ons, and all of a sudden, hundreds of millions of machines were being built and sold."

Dean was there at the beginning. "The operating system that we originally had working with Microsoft and Bill Gates was DOS, and that was the original operating system for the personal computer, the IBM PC. It provided structure in how you interacted with a computer. It provided interfaces that simplified the way a keyboard talked to the central processing unit, and the way the data would be placed on the display, the text and the pictures and all. It allowed you to interface with a printer in a common fashion. Then, we documented the ISA bus and the other information in the system, and I think that made the difference. Documenting it and sharing it allowed others to build on what we had developed and create a compatible environment, which made it the universal tool that it became."

Dean also is careful to point out how this project actually turned out to be a big stepping stone toward the metaverse. "The PC enabled what you might call the virtualization of society. It allowed us to connect beyond just making phone calls or traveling to see each other in person. It allowed us to simultaneously share information with multiple people at multiple times without us being face-to-face in person. It allowed us to store large sums of information, including pictures, audio, videos, and things like that. It allowed us to interact with each other in real time. All of this increased our ability to not only have fun, through gaming and social media and those kinds of things, but to do business more efficiently. It essentially flattened the world; it made things within reach."

A New Level of Freedom

Dean understands the great opportunity the metaverse offers a new generation of users. "The metaverse can be normalizing. In the metaverse, I can be whoever I want to be. I can create my own image of myself in the metaverse. It allows me to interact with people in a neutral environment. My physical view of me and other attributes of me don't necessarily come into play in the metaverse. It can, but it doesn't have to, as an example. It could level the playing field for people that want to be more than what they are... if they want to do business, if they want to even play certain online types of sports, if they want to sell things, if they want to buy things. They're equal. Everybody is on an equal playing field, nobody per se should have an advantage one way or the other."

Dean notes the freedom that the metaverse will offer. "I see the metaverse as something that allows me to do things that I may not be able to do because of maybe my other constraints that people might place on me. I don't have those constraints in the metaverse. It allows me to do business more efficiently, and I can create things that I couldn't create maybe in the physical world. It allows me to be more creative. It allows me to engage people anywhere in the world without me traveling and trying to get to them. I see it as an ability for us to culturally come together, to experience each other in a way that I couldn't experience people before, and learn more about them. Overall, this could increase my knowledge about others and hopefully make the world a better place to live."

Apart from his optimism about the larger social impact of the metaverse, Dean also believes it has the capability to release people's potential. "In the metaverse, the youth of our country should understand that anything they can imagine is possible. There are very few constraints. The only thing that really constrains people is money, time, and risk. As long as you can manage those three things, you'll be successful. Don't stop dreaming; don't let anybody say you can't do something if you really believe in it. Whatever you assume is going to be the limitation disappears with time. The metaverse is a tool people can use like any other tool to build things, to make things happen. It's basically a tool that allows us to create another environment, another world for us to work in, to play in, to interact in."

Because of this potential in the metaverse, Dean says he is "pretty upbeat about the future because there's an endless number of possibilities. There are still a lot of things that can help people work more efficiently, to enjoy things better, to get more information. I think what will be key is how technology is used. For example, there's still a lot of things that we haven't yet figured out. It's interesting that the keyboard is still the decisive choice for entering information. That's amazing to me because the keyboard's been around for such long time, and still no one has figured out quite a more efficient way of entering information and interacting with a computer. I think there are going to be breakthroughs that are going to change that. And I always assumed that printed material would eventually be replaced by a digital tablet, or I would call it electronic paper. I think that's still in progress, but I think we're going to take it one step further. I think ultimately the phone as we know it—the smartphone—will disappear. I will have a means of engaging and interacting with individuals without having to hold something up to my ear or have anything in my hand. I think that's going to be a big breakthrough.

Dean also points out the importance of artificial intelligence in helping the metaverse to realize its full potential. "The use of AI is going to allow me to be smarter. That's the way I want it to be used, to keep me from making mistakes—either new mistakes because we can simulate what will happen, or old mistakes by making me aware of things that have been done in the past which already failed. Better, more real-time access to information that exists will help me. Right now, it's tough to get at it because there's not an efficient way of finding that information. This goes beyond search; it goes beyond traditional AI approaches like a business intelligence. This is a way of allowing me to gain insight in real time, based on my interactions and the things that I'm trying to do."

The advantages of having information in real time are not lost on him. "When I was teaching at the University of Tennessee, I always wanted a device that as I looked at students, it would pop up information about them on the glasses that I was wearing. I would know where they were in their lessons, what grades they had made, if they had a birthday coming up. It would just give me this information in real time, and then I could interact with them without having to memorize everything per se that was going on, and obviously it would give insights beyond what they may think I would know about them. Having that kind of technology on hand, where all this information is readily available and I have access to it, will change the way we interact, making us much, much smarter. It's almost like what the calculator did before we had calculators, and we started to bring calculators in the classroom; that made us a lot smarter. The next-level AI will focus on 'how do I make individuals smarter about what they're doing in their daily lives, in their businesses, in real time, and make their interactions more efficient?' I think that's going to be what I hope will be one of the next big breakthroughs."

Ethics and Access in the Metaverse

Dean also stresses the importance of privacy in this new, interactive environment. "We're going to have to teach individuals how to safely leverage this information. One thing that we have maybe not done as well with technology is teach people the ethical way to use the technology. In the past, ethics tended to be taught in the home, which is fine. But with technology, my parents couldn't teach me ethically how to use technology. Now, I leveraged the ethics they did teach me and applied those lessons to my use of technology. But I think we need to consider a way to reach our young people so they can understand the right and wrong ways to leverage technology, to share information, to interact with individuals. They need to learn the right way to talk to somebody through an interaction that might be more virtual than real. When we first brought on board email, it allowed people to say things that they would never say face-to-face. Obviously, that was the wrong thing. We didn't teach people how to leverage email in an appropriate way. Eventually, people learned, but I think we can do better this time around. As we provide this kind of real-time interactive information, these virtual worlds, these augmented realities, we need to also help people understand the ethics about the development and use of those kinds of technologies."

Part of that understanding relates to the digital divide. In 2002, while at IBM, Dean, along with Rod Atkins, Ted Childs, and other executives, led a signature technology awareness campaign called the Black Family Technology Awareness Week (BFTAW). The campaign was designed to create awareness of the importance of technology specifically in acquiring hardware, internet access, and content. At its zenith, over 8 million people were touched by the program. Its success was the precursor to STEM City USA. As Dean explains, "We weren't sure that was going to work out, but now it's one of the largest virtual environments that exists."

Dean's position about ethics and technology doesn't end there. "Back when we did the original IBM PC, it was going to start to normalize between haves and have-nots. Maybe it's done a little bit of that; I wanted it to do more. I think we need to realize that for people to have access to, and to grow and to be successful, they need certain tools in life, just like we have running water and electricity—things that are important just in general to life. Well, having access to the internet and technologies that are available on the internet and the applications that are available on the internet, I think that's starting to be a right. For example, in school systems, all the students need is something simple like a Chromebook to have access to the metaverse, to STEM City, and to other virtual environments. Because there's so much information and so many courses and things now online, learning needs to move beyond just maybe what we can deliver in the classroom. We need to let students have access to information, somewhat like we used to let them have access to encyclopedias back in the day. You had to go to the library, or some parents were fortunate enough to be able to buy encyclopedias and have them for their students. This is way beyond that."

Dean feels that a simple access device will be the key. "Once we give a child, any child, an access device and point them to STEM City, they will start to self-apply and learn a lot on their own. It's like learning to ride a bicycle. You may have training wheels to start with when you begin to interact with this computing environment. But at some point, they'll throw those training wheels off, and they'll be going 100 miles an hour learning all kinds of things. Just giving underprivileged students access through giving them a $300 access device should be just assumed. It should just be part of our educational system. A child should never go without having access to some kind of tool that gets them on the internet, and maybe this is at the family level. Just like there's a toaster and a microwave and an oven and a toilet in the home, there should be a computer."

And, as Dean said, it doesn't have to be a full-blown computer, because everything a PC used to do will be available in the metaverse. All the students need is a simple access device.

DR. COLIN PARRIS

CHAPTER FOUR:
Colin Parris, Second Life, and the Digital Twin

D r. Colin Parris, senior vice president and chief technical officer at GE Digital, is a visionary who was part of an early version of the metaverse's digital twin component known as Second Life. Parris has been credited with creating the Digital Twin Initiative across GE. A digital twin is a software representation that makes an accurate virtual replica of physical objects, assets, and systems. The digital twin concept is one of the foundations of making the metaverse work on the whole.

Parris spent over a decade at IBM. In one of his positions between 2000 and 2009, Parris led IBM's largest software development organization with a $1 billion budget and 6,000-plus developers across the Americas, Europe, and Asia. He oversaw development, testing, and lab services for all systems software for a $16 billion hardware division. He also led the creation and development of innovative hardware, software, and service solutions for various industries and led the emerging digital convergence business unit.

Today, as senior vice president and chief technology officer for GE Digital, Parris deals with energy transition, green energies, renewables, and electric cars. Parris has acquired patents in network management, multimedia systems, and mobile agents. He has also received multiple honors, awards, and degrees, including a doctorate in electrical engineering from the University of California, Berkeley; a master's degree in the science of management from Stanford University as a Sloan fellow; and a Bachelor of Science in electrical engineering at Howard University. In February 2022, Parris was elected as a member of the National Academy of Engineering.

The Journey Into the Meta Era

When Parris discusses the concept of the metaverse, he compares the transition we're in now to the time before the world had the internet.

"When I think about the metaverse itself, we're on a journey, right? So it's hard to say what it is. It's like the internet; if you'd ask me to describe that in the '80s or '90s, I couldn't do it. So, rather than do that, I think about two things. I think about what changes fundamentally, and what can I do with it. Because this is how I prepare. The two things that change fundamentally to me are integration and innovation. This is all built on a foundation of all the stuff we have now: the internet, the web, cloud capabilities, blockchain, 5G, and virtual reality. But when I think about integration, what we're doing is finding ways to integrate digital islands. It's all about pulling silos together. So, for instance, you have gamers who tell you things like, 'I have these lovely skins that I have in *World of Warcraft,* and I'd love to bring them to *Fortnite.*' You also have consumers who say, 'If my calendar knows I have to attend a meeting, why can't the calendar hook up with the Uber and then actually send an email if I'm late, and why can't all of that be done together?' This is integration. 'Can I integrate the digital with humans in playing games?' More importantly, 'Can I integrate the physical world with the digital world? Can I actually have copies of my cities the way you are doing now with STEM City—a living city beyond virtual worlds. Can I know the energy systems, the wastewater systems, the transportation systems, the healthcare systems? Can I have replicas of them so that I can see what they are like and simulate what would happen in a storm, what would happen in a pandemic, and prepare better for them?' So that's the integration part of it."

Beyond integration, Parris notes that "the innovation part of it is about figuring out what's going to be new. So, for instance, when the internet showed up, it allowed us to fundamentally change parts of society. Amazon changed the commerce process, so now you buy online. Google changed the advertising process. The entertainment process was changed by Apple and by Netflix. So, the metaverse is going to change every one of those processes instantly. The way we teach, everything else is going to change. The more important thing is that it's going to be an opportunity for everyone. And the power we have now in computer systems where I don't need to write code again—because I have low code and no-code—AI helps me get the algorithms right."

Parris details the meaning behind that newfound freedom with the AI. "Instead of having to spend 70 percent of my time learning a tool and 30 percent being creative, I can have 70 percent of my time being creative and 30 percent with the tool. So, now every one of us, especially in our community, can find a way now to use that to change processes. How do I change how we build new sources of energy? How do I change the healthcare system—not just from a technology point of view, but the entire process around it, changing the process the way Amazon and Facebook and others changed theirs back in the dawn of the internet."

Living and Learning: The Digital Twin

Part of that change relies on the digital twin concept. Parris explains the importance of this component to the overall metaverse and the process behind it. "Initially, we create models of things. Whenever we are going to design a new gas turbine on a new jet engine, you create a model, and the model helps you design it correctly. So, the model is really a data representation with algorithms of how it works. And based on that, I could now get the right materials. I could actually do the right design, the right control systems. We also use models when things break. If something begins to break out there, you say, 'Can I look at the model and do various simulations or experiments with the model to understand why it's breaking?' You don't want engines to fail 50 times. If one begins to fail, I want to have a model so I can have the model tell me what's happening."

These working models are also digital twins, which Parris characterizes as "living, learning models." He's already using them in design or when things break. But in the metaverse, he notes, they will be used constantly. Parris says, in that case, "If I use them constantly, I continually send this thing data, and this model continuously changes exactly as the physical engine changes. It's a living model of something that's real—a real jet engine, a real steam turbine. Data is coming into it and changing it, so every flight the jet engine makes, new data comes in, and I can actually change the model because things degrade. I'm learning from other jet engines that are flying."

Parris believes that the living, learning model is one of the many values of the digital twin. "It can give an early warning when something is going to break, like an early warning when a jet engine is going to have a malfunction. Rather than me landing the plane and then deciding, 'Well, there's a light that came on and I have to deplane everyone,' I can get a warning that this thing could possibly be a problem 30 days in advance. With early warnings, I can do a prediction, like how the amount of damage on the failed part might play a role. Sometimes these parts take a year to build, and so I can build a part way in advance so that the plane is not out of commission for too long. I can also perform dynamic optimizations, where I can tell the pilot how to fly the plane to have the lowest fuel consumed and the lowest carbon produced."

Parris explains that the digital twin can do more beyond just modeling to test individual parts. "We have these digital twins of not only our transportation systems but our energy systems, the grid. We have it of our healthcare systems." That concept of a digital twin of entire systems—not just components—is the core to the metaverse. Parris says, "Imagine I have that model, and that model is in a metaverse. It's inside. I can have a model of the city of Chicago, how the energy system works, how the airport works. Now I can use that model to train people on how to react properly if you suddenly have a pandemic. 'Okay, here's how the health system should work.' Because with this model, I can run it backwards and forwards since I have the exact representation of it digitally. This means I can freely do that without affecting the physical world. I can learn a lot and then apply that lesson. Say there's a storm that's going to knock out electricity. How could I predict which storms are coming? What would it do? Where would I position crews? Where would I bring the electricity service back up as much as possible? The metaverse is the perfect tool for me to put these living, learning models up—these digital twins—and combine them to give us a view of warnings, predictions, and optimizations. So, I am a big fan of what's going to happen here."

A New Second Life

Parris has been thinking about this metaverse stuff for a long, long time—all the way back to the early days of a project called Second Life, which was arguably a precursor to the metaverse. Second Life was a virtual world that was created in 2003. It's important to understand how that early version paved the way for what's happening today in the metaverse. Parris explains, "Second Life was a world in which you sold land, you sold avatars, and people did what they wanted. They could do anything they find profitable. They had an economy, so you can get paid for creating content. So, when we started our journey together in 2007, what IBM was trying to do then was two things. They were trying to figure out how I could actually take that virtual world and bring it into IBM behind the firewall and find ways to have our employees increase their productivity. Because this way, you can have remote connectivity; people in different parts could quickly be pulled together and work on something, and you could physically see, 'Could I train people? Could I train people how to go in and replace power boards?' Or, 'Could I design a data center in this virtual world? How do you run the cooling? How do you run the air flows? How do you run the electricity?'

"So, we were using it inside IBM as a collaboration mechanism to increase profitability. At the same time, we were trying to figure out how to make the Second Life world out there and internally in IBM talk together. So, the avatar I had here could go out in Second Life and maybe meet other companies, and we'd collaborate. This is a way we can get our community working with other communities remotely in a shared environment. And now that is taking a new life, especially after the pandemic. So, that's the journey that we started then that we're still on, and I'm delighted to see it happening with STEM City USA."

What's actually different today in the new metaverse when we compare it to its predecessor Second Life? Parris believes there are two big differences. He says, "A lot of it is the human reactions to it. If you look at some of the gaming systems now or the other worlds, the rendering of real capabilities is very different. So, when I look at the pictures, it looks real, almost nearly lifelike. I could begin to immerse myself. It's an avatar, but I can see facial features changing on that avatar. So, the technology below it, all the graphics engines that you have and the bandwidth technology have improved dramatically. The responsiveness and ability to create really interesting fabrics have changed."

Beyond the quality of the rendering, Parris believes the other big difference since the Second Life project is that "humans have changed in even more profound ways. Because of what we experienced in the pandemic, this notion of virtual worlds like we are working on Zoom right now, the notion that we can work remotely, we crossed a hump there. We crossed the hump in saying we have to use these virtual environments to collaborate and in which to deal with some of the hardest problems on the planet."

Parris notes that besides the changes in technology quality and the increase of human acceptance, the third big difference is that "you have some really big names—Facebook, Microsoft—saying they're going to devote billions of dollars towards doing this type of work. That's creating another mirror effect that everybody is investing money in it. Those are the three things I think are key."

You might hear the term Web 3.0 when people talk about the metaverse. Parris is in the midst of working on that now. He explains, "What I spend time on in this new vision of the web is the notion of the Internet of Things. So, we spent a lot of time actually before where you were on the internet, transmitting digital things. A movie is digital; a book can be digital in many cases. Even digitizing money was easy. Now, when you have real physical things, how do you digitize them? So, the Internet of Things, we spend a lot of time doing is taking all that sensor data and putting it in a format where you could represent it digitally and then take an action. It's not enough to get the sensor data in; I've got to have insights. But from the insights, can I then take an action? Can I send a signal to the control system of these jet engines, these steam turbines, machines, and hospitals, and have them take an action? We explore questions like, 'How do you integrate those things so that the virtual world and the physical world come together?' And when they come together, we can use that collaboration power all over the planet, the new computational power we have in these large clouds to actually make a difference, and then we could protect it with blockchain. We could increase the volume of communications with 5G, and we can have AI do some incredible things. So, this is the journey that we are on right now."

Some argue that Web 3.0 is a form of the internet that is more secure and, because of this extra security, will be primarily used by industry. Parris explains that Web 3.0 is three things. "One, it's for the machines. We connect humans to the internet with our cell phones. That's your personal device; all your data is on it. We're connecting the machines and allowing them to phone home with everything you have, so that's the first part of it. The second part of it is connecting the humans who service the machines. And to connect the machines and connect the humans, we need to be secure. We can't have anyone hacking energy systems or medical systems, so that security is huge. Then the third thing is that we must deal with the latency. If I discover a problem, I've got to make sure I can get a signal back fast enough to do something."

AI also plays a role. "This is where you see the vast amount of data coming in. The AI and the humans have to be secure, and then there's the latency that you get from 5G and others. So, it really is about that human-machine connection, secure connection, and bandwidth and latency. These are the basic beginnings of Web 3.0. After that, it will be the apps—exploring the types of applications that can run on top of it."

Parris points out that the layers are key. "Without all of those layers, a true metaverse is not really an open metaverse. You may have some closed metaverses like Second Life, but open metaverses are living and growing in and of themselves. A metaverse is an ability for you to create a digital copy on your own, anytime, any place within that world."

Web 3.0 might be a challenge. Is the United States ahead of the game, or are other countries trying to get protocols in place to beat us? Parris believes that there are "a number of countries" going in and trying to beat us, and this could happen in three or four ways. He says that with "other countries, the focus has to be that people only use things when they can deliver value, especially when you're thinking about Web 3.0

on business. There's value if I can show you how you can save millions of dollars on your jet fuel value, or if I can show you how you can predict and respond to storms when weather patterns show up and what to do to keep the electricity up value. There's value if I can show you, when you take an MRI of a human, how you can get it right quickly with the right diagnosis value. A lot of people are first focusing on applications that show immediate value."

Sovereignty and Standardization

Beyond the immediacy of the value, countries are exploring "standardization." They are wondering if there is a way to standardize data so that the applications and the algorithms that give you value could be used everywhere. An important component of that exploration, Parris notes, is that with standardization also comes things like privacy.

"There's a huge amount of discussion about the sovereignty of data; the data that I should have in one country should remain in one country. So, how am I going to move the algorithms there, so I don't have to copy their data? There are a number of things around the applications, a number of things around the standards, and then a number of things around the governance—whether it be privacy or security—that happen. These are the challenges a variety of countries have been having. And it's very hard to try to get everyone to agree. Europe has a different standard on what data is viewed as private or how the AI could react to that data. China has a different standard. The U.S. has a different standard. So, you've got to find a way to bring these things together. Now, the one good thing is they do come together when it comes to matters of safety, right? If you're worried about jet engines coming out of the sky, you're going to come together. If you're worried about energy problems, you're going to come together. So, we've begun to see certain steps because of the value that could be delivered as well as the inevitable things on the planet we all share. Safety is one, climate is the other, and cyber is the third. So, some of this is happening, but like everything else, it's a journey, and the metaverse will help that journey along. We can see that."

When we look at the metaverse as individuals and consider why it captures the imagination, one thing to keep in mind is that currently, in Web 2.0, wherever we are now, you can't own anything but dot com. With this whole metaverse concept, there's actually the ability to create wealth and to create value in a lot of ways. Decentralization of the technology or blockchain plays a major role.

Parris agrees that decentralization is involved, but he also says, "It's the tooling behind it. Blockchain gives us the ability to actually create social contracts and protect the intellectual property that we have. People hear about this thing known as NFTs, non-fungible tokens—the ability for me to create some piece of intellectual property that's digital and protect it. Right now, people worry because if I create a sound digitally or a video digitally, it can be copied easily. How about if I can create something that cannot be copied? That's the power of the blockchain. If I create this content, and this content is tied into a blockchain where it cannot be copied, and I have the history of it, then I can do transactions with it. I can sell it to you. And I can actually receive the benefit of selling that to you in ways that it's fair. So, it's a distributed contract banking system, all based on the fact that blockchain works the way it does. Blockchain allows you to create content that's uniquely yours, and to protect that content in ways people try copyrights right now, but this is a digital way to protect it."

Parris also talks about the time the new technology saves when creating things. "There's a variety of tools now that have been developed over the last 20 years in which you can quickly create. In my day, I remember we used to have to write assembly programs, and then we wrote the compilers to write the assembly code, and then we wrote the interpreters to write the compilers. Now there's low code. You drag and drop things, and you can create actual code, or there's no-code. You can speak, and it creates code for you. Then there were times when you had to create an algorithm by going through all of the physics. Now with AI, you give it data and it creates the best algorithm. So now what you have is the tools by which your creativity is not limited by the fact that you don't know about the tools. As I mentioned before, I used to spend 70 percent of my time learning how to use the compilers and the systems and 30 percent of my time being creative. Now I can do 30 percent learning a few tools and I get 70 percent of the time for creativity. So, now you have STEM, but you also have creativity, more like STEAM—with 'A' as the artistic part. The new tools have allowed this level of freedom."

Parris is quick to point out that this shift allows for more types of jobs and job opportunities. "You don't have to be a technologist; you can be a marketing person—new ways to market this capability, market the new things that are being sold. You could be a business person—new business models around it. You can be a service person—new ways to service things around that, new ways to develop business processes. So, now the full scope of creativity is actually opened up because of the tools, and you can capture the value of delivering because of the blockchain. Those are the two things I think that are huge right now."

With newfound creativity, of course, comes the desire to protect those creations. The intellectual property approach in this environment is a little different, especially when we're looking at code versus process. Parris states, "When we create new processes in terms of intellectual power, intellectual protection, what you do is really you don't share it, so it's more of a trade secret. If I create a new process by which I evaluate what a customer would buy or the best way to get that customer to buy something, it really counts as a process. I show you these videos at this right time, I segment the customer in a certain way, I offer you these deals at the right time. That's a process. Now, if you want to protect that process, usually what people do is they code the process in a business system. So, for instance, Amazon has a process. It's always interesting to me that they show me things that I should buy. They show me ads on things I should buy, and then they show me deals below if I bundle these things, and they usually get it right. How do they get it right that much? So that's a process by which they're studying 'calling'—they've created a digital twin 'calling,' so to speak—and then they're using that digital twin itself to figure out what to show me and how to encourage me. And maybe they know that I need to see it at least four times before I actually buy it, right? And so that process itself—they codify it; they hide it. They say, 'That's our special process: what to show him, when to show him, how many times to show him.' They don't reveal that; you can't put it in a pattern because everybody knows that becomes a trade secret. Instead, what they may do there is they may actually put that in a little bit of code that they have, and that little bit of code, again, could be kept not as something that's readable, but I could put that as a small module, and that module could be protected by a blockchain."

Parris is careful to point out that there are some exceptions. "You don't always want that, though, because blockchains are visible. There are, however, blockchains that don't let you see what's inside. So, you could protect those things, or you could just not show it. Whenever you create a website or any device in the metaverse, you just don't simply share the process by which you attract people. So, overall, there are two ways to do it: trade secrets or IP."

Beyond blockchain and IP, Parris feels that the metaverse is an important development for tackling larger problems. "We have a lot to solve because now that we have the technology in a stable place, they are now what I call inevitable problems on the planet. Climate, pandemics, inequality in terms of equity, in terms of value of people. How do you use this technology to solve such problems? The aging population we have—how do you solve that problem? It behooves us to take this technology and the innovative process to go after the things that are inevitable on the planet. And then essentially, the next thing after will be space. One planet is interesting, but what if something happens on this planet? Maybe the way for the human race to survive is you need multiple planets in a redundancy."

The GenX, Y, and Z Roles in the Metaquake

Parris sees the next generation playing a vital role. "There's a lot of things left to go do, and I'm looking forward to helping do that. But more importantly, we're helping our community and the young people emerging to join that challenge because here we have a role to play. Like me, I have the opportunities, but I think it's even better for the younger people growing up because as I said, technology has reached a point where it's about your creativity and innovation now. The technology won't stop you and the democratization; you could work remotely where you're now being valued not just for where you came from, but for what you can produce. That's becoming more and more powerful. So, I think we're in for a very interesting new era."

Parris speaks about the resulting democratization, and we need to consider the whole idea of a decentralized metaverse as a reset, where people of color can join the journey and participate. Parris agrees. "I truly believe it is a reset. Now that's not to say we have fixed all those other problems, right? But it is getting better. There's a lot you can do now on a tablet. There's a lot you can do on a phone. It's funny, in my day, you used to have a whole development system and it would cost thousands of dollars to buy tools to have you write code. Now you can sign up with Apple or Android for $99 and you get the system and you can write an app that you can sell to millions of people. So, some of that divide is being reduced. Also, you used to have to go to the best universities to actually get courses that would teach you how to write in C or C++. Now you can go online, get access to Python, get access to many languages, and the languages are easier. You can literally learn the language and you can go to GitHub and you can offer your time and write code, and people will look at your code and see the value of the code you've written. So, it all is getting better. The reset, I think, is here."

Parris points out that we need to be prepared to maximize this opportunity. "Now, if the reset is coming, especially with the metaverse, there are two things I always talk about to prepare yourself: awareness and intent. So, 'awareness'...we are about to change the future; the future's undefined. There is no place for you to simply say, 'Well, somebody's going to tell me exactly what the future is and so I just map it.' No. You've got to go create it, and that gives you value. You've got to increase your awareness. Go and look at the large articles, the write-ups where the large people are talking about things, the Facebooks and the Microsofts, the GEs, the IBMs. People are talking about what's happening. But then go look at gamers too. I mean, you look at Epic and some of them, but then go look at the small things. Look at Sandbox—just one example here—Sandbox is the virtual world built on blockchain. You can keep the content you create, and you see some interesting things. Snoop Dogg has a number of avatars he's selling; there's a whole Snoop Dogg section. People are buying, and he is making good money on that because he is getting paid in Ethereum, a valid currency inside the world of cryptocurrencies. Look at the small things like that because the future is not evenly distributed. The future has arrived in some cases and you've got to be aware of it."

Parris also advises that we need to be ready to commit and invest. "So, you're looking at the big things; you're looking at the small things. The next thing you're looking at are the examples. So, look at the small futuristic things, look at the historical things—that's the awareness part. Now let's talk about the intent or the investment part. Can you commit now? If you want to be a part of this, let's talk about your investments. What's your investment and your talent? Are you going to take a course or two online? No excuse. You go do that. Can you put aside three or four hours a week and go read about these things, write to these people, listen to these podcasts, and watch these videos? 'I'm going to learn something new.' That's putting your time to use your talents to use. 'What am I good at?' If I'm good at the technology side, let's do that. If I'm good at the marketing side, how do I apply that? If I'm good at the sales side, how do I apply that? If I'm good at the administrative side, how do I apply that in this new world? Remember, the same way that the Apples and the Amazons and the Googles transform those processes, we need to do the same thing there."

Capital also plays a role. "The last thing is new money. Invest your money. Don't just invest your time. Sometimes you've got to take a bet, so even if it's a small amount of money, you put it in the things that you control, and now you own equity. Nobody's going to hand you equity that easily. So, think about awareness and then think about investment of time, talent, and money."

When we talk about using the new concept of the metaverse to engage, to add value in the future, Parris points out the differing levels of forecasting expectations. "People think the future cannot be predicted. Well, some parts can. I'll make a prediction right now: I will get older. That's a true prediction. My machines are going to get older. People in the future would like to pay less for things—good prediction. So, when you look at the future, look at some things that are going to happen. You know that the population is going to get older. You know that machines are going to get older; you know that these stones are going to continue battering them. You know that we're going to have to respond to the climate problems we have. Based on that, begin to align yourself—if I know that's true, how do I understand the strengths I have, and how do they translate into me doing something? I always come back to 'Let's figure out knowing your strengths. What can I do? What can I read and understand?' In my world right now, we're dealing with energy transition. People are going to go to green energies, which means they're going to have renewables. They're going to have electric cars. They're going to have to have heat pumps instead of these large oil capabilities. How do I plan my skills there? How do I use the AI to help new changes? If I'm good at marketing, how will you have to market these new services for people so they can reduce electricity costs? If I'm looking at business models, do I understand how I could get someone who has an electric vehicle to sell back electricity to the grid because the grid may not have enough electricity at a given point in time?

"There are things that you can see in the future, and there are things based upon that knowledge you can take your skills and figure out how you apply it. The rest is hard work. You can make the right decision, but then you've got to make the decision right. You've got to put the effort in to shape that in the right direction."

TAKEAWAYS
CHAPTER FOUR

- LIVING AND LEARNING MODELS ARE ONE OF THE MANY VALUES OF THE DIGITAL TWIN.

- OPEN METAVERSES ARE LIVING AND GROWING.

- A METAVERSE IS THE ABILITY TO CREATE A DIGITAL COPY ON YOUR OWN, ANYTIME, ANYWHERE.

- METAVERSE IS AN ESSENTIAL DEVELOPMENT FOR TACKLING CLIMATE CHANGE, PANDEMICS, INEQUALITY, AGING POPULATIONS, AND SPACE.

- BE PREPARED TO MAXIMIZE OPPORTUNITY. WHAT'S YOUR INVESTMENT, AND WHAT'S YOUR TALENT? INVEST YOUR MONEY. THE REST IS HARD WORK.

JOSEPH SAULTER

CHAPTER FIVE:
It All Started with a Game

Believe it or not, some of the technological foundations of the metaverse rely on advances made by the gaming industry going back to the early desktop computer era. Only a little over 30 years ago, Japanese company Nintendo brought Game Boy to the United States, where it became an instant icon of 1990s popular culture. Game Boy and Game Boy Color would go on to sell 118.69 million units worldwide. Since then, the video game industry has become one of the fastest-growing industries in entertainment. In 2012, the gaming industry earned $67 billion, and that was projected to rise to $82 billion by 2017. That era of growth allowed the industry, on the whole, to push 3D rendering to a level where users would expect it in different environments like the metaverse.

Like the rest of the tech world, though, young individuals of color make up a small percentage of the workforce. The International Game Developers Association (IGDA) released a report in 2005 detailing the demographics in the industry, stating that Blacks and Hispanics make up less than 5 percent of game developers. Black youth between the ages of 8 and 18 average about 30 more minutes of gameplay each day than Caucasians. Hispanics average about 10 minutes more. Yet, minorities continue to be underrepresented in the development of the video games and video game content that they love. Professor Dimitri Williams of the University of Southern California has authored several articles on video game content. In one of his studies, Williams reviewed 150 popular video games and determined that they lacked diversity in their content. The results showed that 80 percent of the main characters were Caucasian, less than 3 percent were Hispanic, and, although Blacks made up 10 percent, they were largely confined to the narrative roles of athletes and thugs/gangsters in gaming storylines.

Joseph Saulter, founder and CEO of Entertainment Arts Research Inc. and chairman of the IGDA Diversity Board, believes the answer to this issue is education. Discussing diversity in the development side of the industry, Saulter said, "They don't care if you are Black, white, green, or yellow, so long as you have the tools necessary. There are no guard dogs or water hoses keeping us out of this industry; it's the lack of education, the lack of knowing, because this industry is so ripe for new developers."

Saulter is also a visionary writer, producer, and composer in the music library industry. His Broadway credits include *Hair* and *Jesus Christ Superstar*. Saulter also wrote the drum book for Broadway hit *The Magic Show,* and he received the Drama Desk Award for his role in the Broadway musical *I Love My Wife.* He is a lifetime member of the American Society of Composers, Authors, and Publishers (ASCAP), American Federation of Musicians (AFM) Local 802, New York State School Music Association, and the Professional Composers of America. After graduating with a master's in interdisciplinary/entertainment in 1996 from the State University of New York, Empire State College, Saulter became keenly aware of the growing success of video games. He also discovered that Black people made up less than 2 percent of developers, even though minority groups made up a sizable percentage of the consumer base.

In 2002, Saulter became chairperson of the game design and development department at American InterContinental University. He also created Entertainment Arts Research, Inc. Since then, he has spent years working toward increasing inclusion in the industry. As CEO, founder, and chairperson of EARI, Saulter partnered with industry veteran Johnathan Eubanks to establish the first Black-owned 3D video game development company. The objective was to foster more minority talent and create games reflecting diverse experiences. EARI was also the first Black-owned gaming company traded on the public market. Saulter notes, "We went from 8 cents a share to $12." EARI is still focused on creating games, but it is spreading its reach by pushing toward career-related education and tools.

Saulter began as chair of the IGDA in 2004, where he utilizes his experience as a game designer and professor to discuss and advance diversity issues within the industry.

In 2011, Joseph created the Urban Video Game Academy (UVGA) to promote awareness of career opportunities in the video game industry. UVGA targets minority students. The curriculum of the five-week summer program teaches solid fundamentals in math, physics, and writing—essential aspects of video game development. The students learn the technology basics and skills needed to create their games. The academy spreads awareness of game development to these disadvantaged communities so that they can transform it from a fun hobby into a lifetime career. He is also the author of the book *Introduction to Game Design and Development,* published by McGraw-Hill.

Saulter believes the Black community is an untapped resource for the gaming industry. "The ideas that go into designing, developing, and implementing a game are ripe...our children have a lot of stories that have not been told. The African-American community has stories that have not been told. My company is working on game designs for those stories that haven't been told."

One thing that students need to understand about choosing a career in the gaming industry is that there are many paths that work together to complete the final projects. You have programmers, designers, audio and visual technicians, and business administrators, all with different sets of skills, but working toward a common goal. To break into the gaming industry, Saulter says, "You must bring something to the table...you must have some toolset"—meaning you have to have some background in one of the needed fields. So, programs like the Urban Video Game Academy can be a great way to introduce Black youth to amazing careers in the industry.

If you are a college student right now, one of the most important things you can do to better your future, according to Saulter, is "to find a mentor...people very rarely say no if you ask them to be your mentor."

These professors or professionals can help ease your journey through school and also help you move into areas of opportunity. "The time you do have with your mentor, you need to use effectively. Ask them questions. Ask them for advice. Make sure you are respecting their time as well as your own."

Saulter believes there are new arenas of opportunity opening in the gaming industry, including what he terms the "urbanization of the industry," in which Blacks and Hispanics will need to play a major role. Saulter feels that gaming companies "are looking for new arenas, new games, new designs, something that no one has heard of. I know there are a whole lot of African-American stories that have not been heard yet."

The metaverse and gaming is a combination that excites Saulter, who says, "Most of the time that I've been in this industry, I've been trying to tell African Americans to get in, get on board. There's a train coming down the track. We all are either going to be on that train, or we're not on that train, but the train is not going to stop for you. You're going to have to be at the station when it gets there. Once it stops, then you have to get on and you have to know a lot of things that are going on. So, this metaverse is something that I've been dealing with for a long time." Saulter feels that the metaverse is going to be "an area where we can play in just the way you play every day with the internet. Everybody goes on the internet. Why are they going on the internet? Because it's something that somebody brought to us at a certain point in time, and it's been naturalized. What we're looking at right now is a world of virtual reality, augmented reality, interactive entertainment—all of those things are starting to happen in the real world now. So, you see what's going on in certain areas, but it's not where it's going to be 20 years from now. We're in the beginning of the egg being cracked into the virtual world. Your reality that you are expecting to look at right now, not the actual reality, the Bitcoins, all of the areas of opportunities that NFTs allow for you...these are areas of opportunities that we've got to get into and learn more about."

Sometimes we can refer to the transition Saulter is talking about as A to B, A two B, Adams to bits—everything that's in between that moves us from the physical to the bits, which means virtual reality. It's an augmented reality, but also a reality where you are totally connected. The metaverse, unlike other things, pulls us together. It demands your full attention, which is why we are in the metaverse now—a 2D metaverse. Gaming is also 2D; it was the original metaverse.

Saulter agrees. "As far as development in the world of game design, I was the chairman of the American Intercontinental University, where I spearheaded the game design program for the school that passed the Georgia State certification. Now that is something that is incredibly eye-opening when you go into the 3D arena of it. I've never really been too much of a 2D person, though I do love the comics that are coming out and some of the things that are going on with some of the areas. The 3D arena is where they build digital cities, and a lot of these movies that you see are built in 3D—like *Matrix* city. So, I've been, over the last 15 years, been building out cities, been building out rooms, been building out things. And it's the people that I've met over the years that are the very important part of what's going on."

To be clear, 3D and virtual realities are all different tools. You can have 3D on a 2D platform. That's really important for people in understanding the metaverse because virtual reality is still pretty much limited. In an office space right now, you can put only about 50 people in the room with their headsets. But the metaverse allows you to reach hundreds of thousands of people and give them the true metaverse experience.

Sometimes, it's easier to think of the metaverse in a couple of ways. Most importantly, in the metaverse you have control over your digital self. You have agency—unlike Web 2.0 where information is just being presented to you. In the metaverse, you are truly immersed, and you can do anything you want. You can go wherever you want. You have that control.

Secondly, in the metaverse you generate content if you choose to. It grows; it becomes something bigger than what anyone designed. Beyond that, the most important thing that separates it from 3D and other kinds of pieces is that you can always connect with somebody. There's interactivity. If there's no interactivity, it's not really a metaverse because a metaverse, at the end of the day, is a community. Now, how does all of that happen?

Saulter says, "Look at your web design and your web applications. The only thing you can own on the internet is a dot com. So, when you look at the metaverse—and we are talking about NFTs, we're talking about blockchain, we're talking about all of the areas of opportunity in cyber coins—you can own your creation inside of the metaverse. Let's say you're a very important musician. You're thinking that you need to go to some major company. No, you can start with your music, sell it for a dollar. You'll get 80 cents. Somebody else will get 20 cents. But if they sell your music, now that they own it, you get 80 percent of that transaction. This is going to be the way with everything. We are looking right now at the tip of the iceberg."

Saulter also believes the e-commerce aspect of the metaverse will be integral. He likens it to the transition from conventional banking to automated teller machine (ATM) banking a few decades ago. Saulter explains, "How many people have really looked into what the strength of your digital wallet will be in the next few years? I can remember when there was a point in my life where my father went to the bank, and they said, 'No, you can't come in here. You've got to get this card and go outside.' My father said, 'Man, I don't go outside. I go in the bank. I go in the bank to get my money.' The bank said, 'You can be outside with this card and stick it in this machine out here, punch in your digits and get your money—even after the doors are closed and locked for the day. You don't have to come to me anymore.' My father was so confused. He was like, 'Man, I don't want to do that,' and he was not alone. A lot of people were confused with the fact that all of a sudden, now I don't have any cash in my pocket. I got a card. I swipe the card, I get my money out. It took a while for people to understand the ATM concept and adapt. This is okay. When the world changes so drastically and so quickly, it takes a while to get acclimated. And this same kind of transition is what's going to be happening in terms of the metaverse and how people acclimate. It will be like that transition from old-fashioned banking to ATM machines. Nowadays, it seems strange to look back at the banking world of my father and imagine not having an ATM card to get cash after hours. That's how we're going to look back on this metaverse transition."

Saulter also feels that it's important for people adopting the metaverse to get started. No age is too young. He says, "As a professor of game design and development, I learned very quickly that it's an intense study process to learn any of the applications. Think of it as a football team. Most of the guys that are playing on pro football teams right now started in little league. They played in Pop Warner. They went through all those levels, and they spent a lot of time developing their skills to get to the point where they're accepted into the pros. You have to do that with game design and development. You could pick one little area—might be music—I haven't seen a game that didn't have music in it. Somebody is making some money. I haven't seen a game that hasn't had a 3D character in it—somebody's making some money. The time to get started is now."

When these young people seek careers in gaming tech, they should bear in mind that schools of higher learning now feature programs of study in game design. Here are the top schools in this new field:

1. *University of Utah (Salt Lake City, UT)*
2. *University of Southern California (Los Angeles, CA)*
3. *DigiPen Institute of Technology (Redmond, WA)*
4. *Rochester Institute of Technology (Rochester, NY)*
5. *Massachusetts Institute of Technology (Cambridge, MA)*
6. *Drexel University (Philadelphia, PA)*
7. *Shawnee State University (Portsmouth, OH)*
8. *Savannah College of Art and Design (Savannah, GA)*
9. *The Art Institute of Vancouver (Vancouver, B.C., Canada*
10. *Michigan State University (East Lansing, MI)*

Saulter notes that you don't have to jump right into programming to gain access to the job opportunities of the metaverse. There are other traditional positions for people are who good at managing people. Saulter believes, "You have to know your limits in terms of what you can do. I don't do anything by myself. I have a team of people that are like, if I go to the pros, if I go to the football team, I want one of the biggest guys on my team that can knock down somebody. I need a team of people who can develop and design. If I can't program, maybe I can read it, but I'm not a programmer—not like the guys that I have. When you look at their laptops and they have indentations on the keys, that's a programmer. I don't have indentations on my keys. But what I do have is I put people together to organize, and then you get the best people to work together. And once you get people to work together, the appendages come out. If my arm's not working, somebody else is thinking. It's like an idea. If I have an idea and I keep it to myself, that idea will only get the appendages that I give it. Creativity has to be put in an area where it can be fertilized, where you can grow it, very much like a natural plant. If you don't have those right ingredients for whatever you are trying to build, you're not going to get it. When you have those ingredients, you need to let the spirit of creativity work."

Saulter believes STEM City and places like it are born of the creativity he believes helps businesses succeed. "STEM City came from people who put a whole bunch of things together to try to make something happen. It's just an incredible teamwork to get a game done. And then it's long, long, hard hours to get that game done in terms of game design and development."

Saulter believes people of color trained in STEM will have an opportunity in the gaming segment of the metaverse if they seek the training. He says that "the African-American guys that I know are very, very intense. They're so absorbed. Sometimes you can't come out of that absorption to give yourself an education. But you're going to have to come in to be educated. The game industry is waiting for you. If you are a 3D developer, if you're a programmer, they're waiting for you—they're looking for Black people to come in. What did Facebook just do? Facebook just did $100 million to Black streamers, Black game streamers, and $170 billion in esports."

Saulter says the technology revolution is taking place right now in the metaverse and gaming, and there is an opportunity for people of color to truly be a part of it, because the big guys don't own it yet. Part of the reason why they haven't co-opted it all yet is "the blockchain threw them off. As long as you've got blockchain out there and you have NFTs and people can own something other than the dot coms, then it's a whole different world in terms of equitable opportunity. People can be a part of the metaverse; they can create there rather than going out and buying a store from the people who are going to be putting up metaverses and saying 'buy from us.'"

Everything that you see going forward in this metaverse depends on exactly the same kind of skill sets that Saulter says were relied on to create some of the seminal e-games. And, as Saulter says, that game design experience doesn't have to be used in metaverse e-game settings. "I'm currently working on a metaverse project which involves the metaverse of faith. So, it's a universe of faith-based Christian online collaboration, churches, retail, everything. It's an area of opportunity. We originally designed, developed, and implemented an internet universe of faith. This is years ago...almost probably 10 years ago. And now the new development of that is the metaverse of faith, and that's based on the Verity platform. But it's a huge, huge opportunity. All the people that are dealing in the spiritual world, in terms of religion, they're looking at the opportunity to become active in the metaverse of faith."

As you can see, from gaming to faith, there are so many areas of opportunity here for people of color. Saulter notes again, "And they are looking for people of color. They're looking for you to come into the industry because there's not enough of us in here. And the ones who are in here are looking for you to be able to occupy a certain space. There's a lot of opportunities in diversity. Now, for me, diversity is African American, my community. But diversity is for everybody. It's for all the people who don't have access. I have had a kid who didn't have any hands. And he played games with his feet. And we worked on a controller for the feet. You got people who are LGBT, and there will be a place for them, too. There's no limits in the metaverse." Saulter reminds us, though, that we cannot wait. "You never have an opportunity to make a difference if you're nowhere near it. So, you have to find the keys to getting in. If I have a key to help you out, you have it. If I can help you make $1,000 more than you're making today, I would do it because there's enough money in the game design and development metaverse where everybody could sit at the table, and there's enough food to go around for all."

And it all started with a game, so don't underestimate the power of gaming and the gaming industry. As Saulter says, "Look at your children. If they're upstairs playing the game, that's okay. My barber's son from 3 years old started playing one of the games. He was asked by Sony to join a team at 13 years old, and he's making thousands of dollars now. Just let your children know that it's okay to play games."

Gaming is also more than just playing at home. Electronic sports, known as esports, is a form of multi-user gaming with competitions that feature professional players. They're paid to play video games in tournaments. This form of gaming has grown to such a degree that professional sports teams have e-teams and players representing them. Esports is the latest in competitive entertainment. Fans watch in person via live streams online, or even on major networks such as ESPN. Esports has become one of the fastest-growing industries in entertainment.

With this growth potential in mind, Hampton University has become the first HBCU with an esports gaming lab. Historically, as we know, Blacks and Hispanics in the United States have been "late to the game" or "sidelined" during technological advances. However, Hampton University plans to help close that gap by being at the forefront of esports. "Esports is a billion-dollar economy that we are not a part of," says sports management professor David Hughes in an interview with *USBE* magazine. When the opportunity presented itself with esports, he decided it was time to take a shot. "I wanted to do some-thing new. So, the leadership here gave me the opportunity to explore, and I was able to take advantage." Hughes notes that esports is also "the new emerging thing in sports management...with us being able to get the technology to start the esports lab, we will be the first HBCU to offer esports curriculum, putting us ahead of the curve. We're also looking to offer certificates in coaching esports."

Much like other areas in STEM, there is a strong need for African Americans in this side of the gaming industry. Hughes explains, "There are some stats that say Blacks make up 75 percent of the consumers of video games, and less than 2 percent participate in creating them. By having this lab at Hampton, we are now helping to fill that void of diversity in the esports space."

Several other states throughout the country are now preparing to offer esports as part of their middle school and high school varsity programs. This will, in turn, drive a need for esports coaches. Here's where Hampton University steps in—offering an esports coaching curriculum that will prepare African Americans with the right tools to secure leadership positions in this field. "Our lab also will have an innovations center," says Hughes. "Students can learn how to create video games and pitch to venture capitalists. Beyond that, I want music students to score these video games. I'm looking forward to the opportunity for cooperative economics with the students here at Hampton. When you think of Black people in esports, I want you to think of Hampton University. I want Hampton to provide the most Black esports coaches, I want us to produce video games, and I want students to be extremely successful in esports."

As the metaverse grows alongside the rise in esports, it is expected that HBCUs will increase their support for students in these new industries. Courses and fields of study already exist to assist young developers looking to get started, and this wise expansion into esports by Hampton demonstrates the interest in offering students cutting-edge opportunities. As the experts have told us, this is the right time for individuals of color to seek training in the metaverse and metaverse-related fields.

DR. CHRISTOPHER JONES

CHAPTER SIX:
Chris Jones and the Military

D r. Christopher T. Jones, winner of the 2016 Black Engineer of the Year award, is a former president of technology services at Northrop Grumman Corporation. He also is a retired U.S. Air Force officer and retired member of the Connecticut Air National Guard. In 2021, he was elected to the National Academy of Engineering for leadership of defense logistics, sustainment, training, and system readiness in support of U.S. national security. Jones's work with the U.S. military, in academia, and with defense contractors provided him a direct role in AR and VR environments and three-dimensional simulations. Jones has played a leading role in what *Wired* magazine described recently in its feature, "The U.S. Military Is Building Its Metaverse."

Jones's career experience offers a unique perspective on the development of the metaverse and its value. As president of the Technology Services sector for Northrop Grumman, he led a $4 billion organization of more than 13,000. He supported the U.S. Department of Defense, Department of Energy, Department of Homeland Security, Department of State, Department of the Interior, NASA, and the U.S. Postal Service.

Jones also directed and oversaw engineering, technology development, and integration into aircraft, avionics, and other aerospace systems for the U.S. Army, U.S. Air Force, U.S. Navy, Royal Air Force, and Royal Australian Air Force. His organization supported more than 60 significant subsystems and different type-model-series of aircraft, including bombers, fighters, uncrewed aircraft, helicopters, electronic aircraft, cargo and refueling aircraft, and commercial-derivative aircraft. The sector provided life cycle logistics, aircraft, military vehicle sustainment and modernization, military training, and mission readiness solutions. Jones was also instrumental in the airborne early warning and battle management command and control, where he was responsible for all U.S. E-2 Hawkeye support and international E-2 Hawkeye programs. He provided technical leadership during the aircraft design, development, production, and fielding and was a vital member of the technology insertion and integration teams.

Before joining Northrop Grumman, Jones worked at Sikorsky Aircraft Corporation, where he led analysis, flight tests, and research on innovative rotorcraft technologies. He was Sikorsky's technology lead on the RAH-66 Comanche helicopter program and served as a chief systems engineer for the Naval Hawk program.

Jones's experience makes him unmatched as an expert evaluating the advantages of the metaverse and how it will support the military and its machines and systems. He considers the role of the metaverse from his perspective as both a former military officer and also as a private sector leader in training systems and logistics and 3D simulation training. "We have to prepare people who are eventually going into combat to have as much proficiency, confidence, and ability as possible so that when they're in operations and things don't go according to plan, they can fall back on the training we've provided. And we need to prepare them for this, of course, without harming them while training." A safe "test drive" of these scenarios is something the metaverse can offer.

Jones notes the advantages of training with the assistance of today's technology. "When I joined, a lot of activity was a manual. You would read a manual and replicate maintenance on a jet engine. Thirty years on, we've evolved into simulations. Someone flying an aircraft, operating a ground vehicle, a ship, or another piece of equipment has a simulator. The easiest way to think about that is from an aircraft standpoint: You're in a simulator, flying, and you have a joystick and a throttle that evolved to where you network the simulations. SIMNET was a simulation network that started in the '80s and '90s. Things have progressed now to where you have this vast distributed network of simulators and training to practice an individual task, like a repair. In conflict, you'll be operating multiple aircraft; there'll be land forces. Today, you could link all air assets with the ground with a simulation link. You can also do that with ships in the virtual training environment."

The Connection Between Gaming and the Military

Jones points out that gaming has also played a role in building these training systems, helping to set the foundation for the metaverse. "If you go back to the '80s and '90s, some military folks had the foresight to realize the importance of investing in games. I'm a gamer. So, I had a character in Second Life. I was a big fan of SimCity. It went from 2D to 3D, then to Sims, up to Fortnite, Roblox, Mindframe, Call of Duty, and Doom. I am well versed, especially on the user side. Some leaders had the foresight to look at the gaming industry because a large segment of its content has to do with what we can refer to as defense or warfare. There's a significant element of that. How could that be leveraged for the military? They came up with a couple of angles. One involves recruiting. The Army and other branches used game technology and partnered with game companies to create games. It's more on the land forces side to help recruit folks into the military.

The connection between technology and gamers does not end there. "The second angle is to use that same technology for training. Think about Call of Duty or other games; they're built on the engine around those used for training ground forces. Think of a Marine or soldier with a hand weapon in ground forces combat. Think of an air force from a simulation side. The amount of money and investment going into games has bolstered the military's ability to recruit and train its soldiers, aviators, sailors, and now, space guardians."

Jones points out the connection between youth culture, gaming, and our branches of national defense. It's a noteworthy link. "When you think about the country's defense, it's done by 20-year-olds. Regardless of what's in the movies or what we're told, those in combat who don't return are in their 20s. A decade from now, it'll be in the hands of people that today are 10 or 15 years old. It's essential—having worn a uniform for 20-

some years—to ensure we're not just keeping up with that generation but also leveraging their skills. A large subset of that was developed because of all the games they've played in their lifetime."

On submarines, aircraft carrier landings, and looking at refueling of a large aircraft, it's young 18- to 21-year-olds that we call to duty. It's essential that we provide opportunities to help protect those young people who are risking their lives to defend our country. New technology in the metaverse will support that goal. Jones says, "We now have virtual reality systems where an aviator works on an aircraft or where soldiers operate on a tank. You can put on goggles, manipulate the virtual world, and practice. They can reach for equipment. What's coming will be augmented reality. They'll wear a device to look out in the real world to see everything. For example, the engine will highlight which tube or wire is defective on their goggles, and then they could look down at their tool chest, which is highlighting which tool to grab. They'll be able to make the repairs all with that augmentation."

This is similar to Dr. Parris's points about the importance of the digital twin and modeling. Jones agrees. "What I see in the metaverse going forward is they'll be able to be immersed in a 3D world. They will feel like they're standing next to someone, even though that person is miles away. They'll be able to interact. The trainee will be able to point and say, 'What did you do with this? What did you do with that?' They'll be able to have feedback in real time. The person will be able to interact with other classmates in this 3D virtual, and they'll be able to see input via devices and sense it. We'll go from a virtual standalone to a 3D environment where you're right next to somebody explaining how to fix whatever needs to be repaired. It's not just you, alone with a simulator. So then, when you return to the real world, you'll have augmented reality and be able to see what you're doing with aids on a screen."

Jones points out the equally important advantages of such an environment once it moves away from the maintenance area. "If we translate that into combat, some systems now exist where pilots can fly and train. You don't want to have a lot of planes flying around because it's dangerous. And so, what you will have in the future is they wear goggles.

They'll look up in the sky and project what they see on goggles. It could be another plane. And their aircraft will be launched, so they're not close to the plane the other person's in. And if you can project that plane, you can project many things."

Jones also points out the value in scenarios that occur in combat even when they do not involve direct fire. "Something as seemingly simple as air-to-air refueling is hazardous. What if the person in the fighter can project the refueling aircraft, and they do that repeatedly—not in a simulation, but on their goggles? Think about soldiers in combat and training. You could project enemy combatants and launch things if they're wearing goggles. They could be in the field, but you can project that training. Then they can go to a 3D world and interact in a way they could in 2D now—but with soldiers, debriefings, and training in that entirely immersive world. That's the next step when you think about military simulation training. Then you can take that as far as operations, logistics, and medicine—it all could have the same impact."

Jones also notes that there is a human element to the metaverse that is important in a different way: basic communication and how it relates to soldiers' morale. "When our folks overseas want to reconnect with their overseas family and their families in the U.S., they do that via 2D. The metaverse of the near future, they can be immersive, where they can interact with their family as though they're right there with them. It's important to take care of the people, the professionals in harm's way, and ensure they're connected with their loved ones. Their families are part of the military."

An often overlooked fact is that the military helped create the internet. A lot of the research was done by the Department of Defense. Jones believes the metaverse will be a new access point, a gateway for people to become interested in technology careers in the military and technology as a field in general. Jones thinks of the metaverse as a place where "you can be part of the creation of it, or you can use it. The internet's the same. You can help write code, be a software engineer, work on routers, and transfer data and the cloud. You can do all those things, or you can leverage it. You can have a restaurant that leverages the internet. So, you can have a brick-and-mortar place where people come and get your food. They can order it online and go and get it, or they can order it online and deliver it. That's a standard use of the internet. I see the metaverse as the same. If you look at some building blocks: augmented reality, virtual reality, data science, data analytics, and artificial intelligence—those are good fields to get into. So, if you're early career, or even mid-career getting up to speed on what success in those fields means, you explore before you decide whether that would be something you'd like. The metaverse can give you a visual impression of what that might be like. Let's say you were an artist creating a movie. The metaverse can allow you to test drive the visuals and how that content would look. Remember, at some point in the past, there were no movie theaters. There were no movie sets. There was none of that. Then there were inventions based on projecting sound, visual aspects, and distance onto a screen for people to look at. The early adopters became the visionaries because they were able to see the potential impact. The metaverse today will have the same effect."

Jones also has some ideas about the connection between opportunities provided by the military for young, up-and-coming businesses. "If you're a small business, you want to impact your business today and get payroll next week. You could go to the Air Force Research Laboratory [AFRL] and see what they're investing in today, listen to their leaders, listen to the podcast, and figure it out. They're all disseminating what they're looking for in the next one, three, and five years, and they break that down. You can go by technology readiness level, TR [technology readiness] level one, two, and three. Some organizations were specifically designed and created to help small businesses and help them transition from civilian commercial technology to the military. Those organizations exist, and they live on the internet. If you're not there already, go to Northrop Grumman and Boeing. They all have laid out their vision for the near term, three to five years, and some longer. So, if you're a small business, what they're looking for today exists. If you're more startup, you've got three to five years. Again, I'd go to the Office of Naval Research, AFRL, and Army Research Lab to map out the technologies, whether it's hypersonics, artificial intelligence, machine learning, or data analytics."

Jones also sees options for students. "Some of the fields that'll be important are data science, data analytics, and almost anything related to STEM. Those are all applicable to the metaverse. If I'm an undergraduate, I would be sure to be conversant in basic computer and IT. You don't want to get caught up in fads and have that supersede what you like to do. Our folks tend to make that mistake. They kind of chase jobs or prestige. But if they're honest, they don't like it; they don't perform as well. So, for a student, think about what you want to do. If you like code and software, there are a lot of software development companies. If you're more of a hardware person geared towards router, do that. If you're more of an engineer, think about training or equipment operations and how you could use a metaverse. And I'd say for students as well, watch your videos, read your books, get different opinions. I would get all of that and then make your own decision."

TAKEAWAYS
CHAPTER SIX

- CHECK OUT THE AIR FORCE RESEARCH LABORATORY (AFRL) WEBSITE AND SEE WHAT THEY'RE INVESTING IN TODAY.

- LISTEN TO AFRL LEADERS AND LISTEN TO THEIR PODCASTS.

- FIND ORGANIZATIONS THAT HELP WITH TECHNOLOGY READINESS TO TRANSITION FROM CIVILIAN COMMERCIAL TECHNOLOGY TO MILITARY. VISIT NORTHROP GRUMMAN'S WEBSITES.

- GO TO THE OFFICE OF NAVAL RESEARCH AND THE ARMY RESEARCH LAB TO MAP OUT THE TECHNOLOGIES, WHETHER HYPERSONIC, AI, MACHINE LEARNING, OR DATA ANALYSIS.

Learning about robotics at a recent Women of Color in STEM Conference

CHAPTER SEVEN:
Artificial Intelligence, Quantum Mechanics, and Metaverse Jobs

Quantum information can be in two places at one time, but my concern is that we're not going to be any place at one time.

Artificial intelligence is integrating more and more into our workplaces and personal lives. Almost everyone has experienced commonplace AI examples like Google's "suggested searches" dropdown bar, along with website access CAPTCHA images (the ones that make you click every photo containing a car or stoplight before you can log onto a platform). These are examples of what Dr. Jeffrey Welser at IBM Research calls "point solutions"—AI applications with very narrow goals in comparison to what the technology is expected to do in the near future, especially in the metaverse.

M.G. Spencer of Morgan State University agrees. He says, "AI is already in society on a very subtle level. It's the disembodied voices you hear on the phone when you inquire about a bill, or it's the robotic machines sold in TV ads that will clean up floors on their own. The influence of AI can be seen in Pandora and Amazon software; these all learn your browser history and recognize your personal trends so that ads on web pages are tailored specifically for you."

Spencer points out that the big-picture perception of AI goes beyond the point solution model. "When most people think of artificial intelligence technology, they typically imagine the kind of Utopian future seen on mid-century TV programs like *Star Trek*. In that idyllic world, there was a diverse group of people journeying into space and exploring new galaxies using extremely advanced technologies. The technology in our imaginations and in Hollywood portrayals is often viewed as the promise for positive things in the future. But there is another possible future that technology can bring: a dark, dystopic future where society is more strongly divided between the digital 'haves' and 'have-nots.'" This is especially true when we consider the future role of AI in our lives and what it might mean for us in the metaverse.

Man vs. Machine Learning

Spencer says that as AI continues to evolve, "It will appear in both stand-alone and human augmentation forms. Both implementations have the capacity to make obsolete many blue-collar jobs, and, surprisingly, a large number of white-collar jobs. Not only will AI impact (and possibly eliminate) jobs that require hand skills, but it will also impact careers where the job function is repetitive in nature. Consider the technological innovation of Uber. Uber has created a number of employment opportunities, particularly for people of color and in lower economic brackets. These new jobs give people the ability to earn extra wages to supplement their income. But self-driving cars are on the horizon, and the technology for self-driving cars is rapidly improving. Self-driving cars (which, ironically, Uber is also investing in) will eliminate or drastically reduce the job gains made by Uber drivers. AI is already being employed to make and deliver pizzas as well as manufacture automobiles. The trend will only increase."

Robotics and intuitive machines now do the work of hundreds of employees, and, over time, these will increase the return on investment for those organizations—creating long-term profits. Machines don't take vacations, sick days, or lunch breaks, and they don't work in specified periods of time. They are always on and always working. When we think of the possibility of a "dark, dystopic future" mentioned by Spencer, this involves the potentially disruptive impact of AI in many employment sectors, including manufacturing, shipping supply chains, and product-to-delivery markets.

But we also have AI focused on portions of the knowledge workforce. AI is being developed with the capability to think like humans. This is what we call machine learning, where the machine is trained to think, reason, or process data in a similar way to humans. We are in the early stages of this phenomenon, also known as the "supervised machine learning phase," where much of the training is being driven by businesses and the data scientists who create algorithms that mimic the physical world. Those algorithms are constantly being tuned to past historical data that we already know the answers to so that the machine can give us some indication that it is catching on to the process. If you analyze past information to process the incoming data with the actual outcome that occurred, you can now "teach" a machine to learn the incoming data, derive the outcome, and measure the accuracy. This is how we understand the maturity of the machines running specific algorithms and platforms.

The ideal goal is to achieve unsupervised machine learning. In the unsupervised learning state, AI will no longer need to be trained; it will start to train itself. This is similar to how we humans perceive, reason, learn, and take in data based on our senses, reasoning capabilities, and acquired knowledge. We likely are in a 10- to 15-year span of seeing unsupervised learning enter the market across every vertical possible: financial, retail, government, manufacturing, and supply chains.

When you start to consider the introduction of AI, one has to look at what is necessary as an employee or a career professional today to make sure we are on the non-disrupted side of the curve. If I am looking to avoid disruption from AI, I have to look at STEM as a knowledge workforce base, no matter where or what particular role I play. Whether it involves marketing, sales, or finance, STEM is going to be there as an opportunity to begin redesigning professional career paths in order to take advantage of the number of upcoming opportunities, especially in the metaverse, that will undoubtedly involve STEM in some form. This doesn't necessarily mean workers will have to be mathematicians or the best coders. What it will mean is that they will have to have more intimate knowledge of technology and how it can be used so that it can spur innovative thought.

Take, for example, the clothing retail industry. That may seem like the polar opposite of a STEM-focused career. But if I mentioned the use of geolocation data or the blending of brick-and-mortar omni-channel and digital experiences, then technology becomes the most important topic of that retail industry conversation. If I track someone on the phone and watch very closely what they're searching for, and they happen to search for a jacket and walk past Macy's, I can pop up a Macy's coupon for a jacket of that type to drive an impulse reaction on their part to head inside Macy's to buy that jacket. Or I can pop up an e-commerce link to say, "Buy the jacket online, and we'll deliver it to you." Just like that, retail becomes a STEM technology market and less of a face-to-face, people-to-people market. If I'm in retail, I should begin to look at technology and begin to understand how to leverage and adopt it to be more relevant in my professional area.

Similarly, as a cashier at the traditional point of sale, I can now look at the opportunities with mobile applications or processes to see the historical perspectives of time-based or time series data that analyzes optimal shopping times. I can begin to contribute to that discussion and start providing insight without ever understanding how technical solutions are going to work. Before technology can be implemented, processes have to be understood. To be a part of the innovation of AI, as opposed to being disrupted by it, I have to look at how, when, and why I do things within my organization. That's the future of knowledge workers—not to be intimidated by AI but to continue to look at insights to create innovative ways of driving process automation and workforce efficiency.

Workforce Disruption

Spencer says we need to keep in mind, though, that it's not that simple. He says we have to keep in mind past labor market concerns. In previous times of industrial change, "when the majority of society catches a cold, Black communities catch pneumonia, figuratively speaking. The impact that AI job transfers will have on communities of color will likely be much more dramatic than it will have on white communities. Without a dramatic paradigm shift, it will be divided and extremely polarized. Resulting job loss and job opportunity loss will parallel the situation in the energy sector. The sharp reduction in dependence on coal for energy left communities in the Midwest desolate and outside of the economic revolution. Similar situations can be envisioned in big cities like Baltimore. Those who understand and can relate to the digital revolution understand what's happening with AI and computer technology, and they have a sense of preparedness for the emerging jobs and careers. Those communities that do not have the education, are not prepared, and do not know how to seek out the necessary training will fall victim to the ever-changing winds and trends of technology. As a consequence, they will fall further back economically."

Spencer expects HBCUs like Morgan State to provide "a safety valve for society, a way out, and a gateway to the middle class. But this means that students need to commit to a STEM-based program with the metaverse in mind." Spencer notes that "we have to take advantage of the current state of technology. If students seek only training in certificates or back-to-school programs, they will only be prepared for jobs that exist today. Those jobs can be lost in a very short period of time. All projections that we are seeing now indicate that computer-related jobs are going to increase by at least 25 percent over the next few years. We know that computer-related careers will grow because of the metaverse. These include careers in AI technology, deep machine learning, cyber security, and computer programming. Students of color need to consider training that allows them to adjust to a rapidly shifting employment landscape. That way, the technological revolution will lead them to a Utopic future, not a dystopic one."

Spencer is not alone. Dr. Margaret Martonosi of the National Science Foundation is currently researching how AI might affect a range of fields and industries, including the metaverse. "We're looking at AI's potential use in smart communities, healthcare, robotics, and elsewhere," she says. "NSF is the nation's basic science research agency, so while other agencies might zoom in on human health, for example, our mission stretches across all of the scientific topics." Much of the NSF's focus is on funding initiatives, such as the MSI (Minority-Serving Institution) Research Expansion Program, which, as Monorosi explains, "seeks to enhance research capacity at HBCUs."

Increasing diversity is a mission shared by Dr. Rediet Abebe, a junior fellow at the Harvard Society of Fellows and assistant professor of computer science at the University of California, Berkeley. Abebe believes that AI can play a valuable role in solving diversity, equity, and justice issues. "It could help us deal with questions like how to measure poverty, discrimination, and inequality, or how to best allocate the resources we have," says Abebe, also a co-founder of Black in AI, a nonprofit research community. "Even if we're not dismantling these oppressive structures, we can help move the needle."

Dr. Fei Fei Li, co-director of Stanford University's Institute for Human-Centered Artificial Intelligence, agrees. "We work with more than 16 colleges and universities around the country to create summer programs for students from underserved and underrepresented communities," she says. "Our goal is to create a pipeline of students from all backgrounds and walks of life to become tomorrow's leaders."

There is a need for talent in this blossoming market. With algorithms growing more complex, large-scale systems getting more efficient, and the availability of data growing by the day, both private companies and research institutions need talented people to help them leverage artificial intelligence to its full potential.

As Dr. Darsana Josyula, professor of computer science and director of the Autonomous Technologies Lab at Bowie State University, says, "AI is an open frontier. Its real-world applications are new enough that trained AI practitioners do not yet exist at the scale they are needed. The challenge facing organizations right now is how to find and retain future talent with state-of-the-art knowledge. This is where our institutions play a key role."

Workforce disruption has been a regular occurrence for hundreds of years. Every time disruption enters a market, new markets are created. Such is the case with this digital age and the introduction of AI, especially in the metaverse. By putting eyes and ears on such opportunities, workers will be able to take advantage of those AI market opportunities and forge their own paths into the new digital marketplace of the metaverse.

Societal Shifts Through Quantum Mechanics

Another important consideration for workers is the role that quantum mechanics will play in the Meta Era. At the Quantum Information Science panel of the 2021 Black Engineer of the Year conference, Nobel-winning physicist William Phillips spoke about the challenges and opportunities of what he calls the "second quantum revolution"—the scientific period starting in the late 20th century defined by an effort to understand and find applications for the features of quantum mechanics. "In digital technology, bits of information are binary; they're either zero or one," he explains, "but in quantum mechanics, something could be zero, one, or both zero and one at the same time. If a qubit can be both zero and one at the same time, this means that a computer can do lots of computations with a lot of inputs at once."

This type of information, he says, could be used in the development of "computers that can do the kinds of computations we couldn't dream of before, communications more secure than we've ever imagined, instruments which can measure things better than we could've ever thought possible. The kinds of things it will give us are unimaginable right now."

Phillips is not alone in recognizing this potential. In September 2020, IBM announced the world's first quantum education and research initiative for HBCUs. The IBM-HBCU Quantum Center is a multi-year investment designed to prepare and develop talent at HBCUs from all STEM disciplines for the quantum future. Led by Howard University, the IBM-HBCU Quantum Center offers access to its quantum computers and collaboration on academic, education, and community outreach programs. It will focus on developing students through support and funding for research opportunities, curriculum development, workforce advocacy, and special projects.

IBM also said it would invest $100 million in technology, assets, resources, and skills development through partnerships with additional HBCUs through the IBM Skills Academy Academic Initiative. "We believe that to expand opportunity for diverse populations, we need a diverse talent pipeline of the next generation of tech leaders from

HBCUs," said Carla Grant Pickens, chief global diversity and inclusion officer at IBM. "Diversity and inclusion are what fuels innovation, and students from HBCUs will be positioned to play a significant part of what will drive innovations for the future like quantum computing, cloud, and AI."

Dr. Kayla Lee, who championed the initiative that brought quantum computing resources to HBCUs, has seen similar programs expand at other campuses. Lee, who has a Ph.D. in systems biology from Harvard University, is a third-generation HBCU graduate of Hampton University. As a product manager at IBM Research, she leads strategic initiatives to help create and grow a global quantum computing community. "When IBM launched the IBM-HBCU Quantum Center last September, our goal was to collaborate with historically Black colleges and universities in a way that would advance not only quantum information science but also STEM-based opportunities for these traditionally underrepresented communities."

Lee joined IBM Quantum in 2018. As an industry consultant, she worked with Fortune 500 companies to explore potential quantum computing applications across industries, including healthcare and life sciences, financial services, media, and entertainment. She continues to lead initiatives to grow the IBM Quantum Community with new global partnerships. "I'm motivated to make complex, scientific topics like quantum computing and emerging technology not only accessible but also engaging. I partner with students, researchers, and clients worldwide to address technical challenges with new computing technologies," Lee says. "As a proud graduate of Hampton University, I was excited to launch the IBM-HBCU Quantum Center, a multi-year investment from IBM to bring together HBCUs to build quantum research and education capabilities. This center will drive diversity and inclusion in quantum computing and provide new opportunities for historically underrepresented communities."

The IBM Quantum Network is a community of more than 140 partners consisting of Fortune 500 companies, academic institutions, startups, and research labs that work with IBM to advance quantum computing. There are more than 300,000 registered users of programming tools IBM Quantum Composer and IBM Quantum Lab. IBM is driven to make quantum software easier to use and more accessible. These tools, which replace what was formerly known as the IBM Quantum Experience, enable you to build quantum circuits and run experiments that can ultimately help accelerate research development and applications using IBM's quantum computing software.

The IBM Quantum community executes more than 1 billion hardware circuits per day on real hardware and simulators using Qiskit, an IBM-developed open-source software development kit for working with quantum computers' level of pulses, circuits, and algorithms. Researchers have published more than 400 research papers using results from IBM Quantum systems. Their view is that we experience the benefits of classical computing every day, but there are challenges that today's systems will never be able to solve. We do not have enough computational power on Earth to tackle problems above a specific size and complexity. To have a chance at solving some of these problems, we need the computing power quantum can offer.

All computing systems rely on a fundamental ability to store and manipulate information. Current computers control individual bits, which store data as binary 0 and 1 states. Quantum computers leverage quantum mechanical phenomena to manage data. To do this, they rely on quantum bits, or qubits. Qubits are the fundamental elements of a quantum computer that process information. Three quantum mechanical properties—superposition, entanglement, and interference—are used in quantum computing to manipulate the state of a qubit.

Superposition refers to a combination of states we would ordinarily describe independently. To make a classical analogy, if you play two musical notes at once, what you will hear is a superposition of the two notes. This phenomenon gives qubits their exponential computing space potential.

Entanglement is a famously counterintuitive quantum phenomenon describing behavior we never see in the classical world. Entangled particles behave together as a system in ways that cannot be explained using classical logic—what Einstein called "spooky action at a distance."

Finally, quantum states can undergo interference due to a phenomenon known as phase. Quantum interference can be understood in a similar way to wave interference; when two waves are in phase, their amplitudes add, and when they are out of phase, their amplitudes cancel. This helps users determine the accuracy of an execution done on a qubit or set of qubits.

Denise Baken, president of Shield Analysis Technology, LLC, is another industry leader who recognizes the potential in this area. "Quantum brings with it a vast capability to change lives and drastically improve the economy," she says. "The quantum computing market is expected to leapfrog from its current $220 million to $2.2 billion by 2026, only four years from now." However, she explains that the United States is significantly behind other countries regarding quantum development. "When you think about the fact that China deployed a quantum satellite in 2016, you must recognize that we're behind the curve," she says. "This raises major concerns about our national security, particularly in relation to cryptography."

Baken cites a lack of education around quantum mechanics and information as one of the biggest causes of the power imbalance between the U.S. and other countries when it comes to technology. "There's a lack of literacy across all economic and social levels. We have to recognize that this is a national security imperative, one our country must address if we're to compete in the emerging quantum economics environment."

She sees the knowledge gap as an opportunity for quantum research organizations to embrace the untapped potential of minority communities, which are severely underrepresented in the scientific community. "In addressing this dearth of quantum literacy, we have to make sure there's a place for all at the policy and decision-making tables," she says.

Lily Milliner, executive vice president of Delmock Technology, agrees that it's vital to encourage minority students and business owners to get interested in quantum technologies. "I encourage minorities to take a look at this," she says, emphasizing the fast growth of this field.

"Quantum information is going to show up in culinary, aerospace, law enforcement, and so many areas we don't even understand yet." She notes that, "Quantum information can be in two places at one time, but my concern is that we're not going to be any place at one time. If minority businesses do not take this opportunity to go into the quantum industry, we're not going to be at the table at all."

Phillips nods in agreement. He says there is no lack of opportunity for those willing to venture into this growing field. "At the University of Maryland Joint Quantum Institute, industrial entities like Google and IBM are coming to us *begging* for more quantum-trained people," he says. "So, if you're looking for a job and you know the difference between a bit and a qubit, they need people like you in their operations."

It's time for potential investors and workers to look toward AI and quantum technologies as a gateway into the future and the metaverse.

TAKEAWAYS
CHAPTER SEVEN

- ENCOURAGE MINORITY STUDENTS AND BUSINESS OWNERS INTERESTED IN QUANTUM TECHNOLOGIES.

- QUANTUM INFORMATION WILL SHOW UP IN CULINARY, AEROSPACE, LAW ENFORCEMENT, AND MANY AREAS WE STILL NEED TO UNDERSTAND.

- GOOGLE AND IBM ARE LOOKING FOR QUANTUM-TRAINED PEOPLE.

- KNOW THE DIFFERENCE BETWEEN A BIT AND A QUBIT.

- AI AND QUANTUM TECHNOLOGIES ARE A GATEWAY INTO THE FUTURE AND THE METAVERSE.

STEM CITY·USA

Discussing career opportunities at a recent
BEYA STEM Global Competitive Conference

CHAPTER EIGHT:
Professional Skills and Career Opportunities

One company after another is pouring hundreds of millions of dollars into building the new metaverse. As Dr. Parris told us, the ramping up of investment by the big tech companies in the metaverse has pushed the concept forward much faster. Several companies are now willing to take on the challenge—because those who succeed will reap the financial rewards. Estimates vary wildly, but some analysts say the market value of the metaverse sector will reach $800 billion by 2024 and could eventually climb into the trillions. The pandemic also accelerated the speed of development, and that means the creation of countless new tech jobs in the coming years.

The possibilities for selling virtual items, advertising, and other real-world analogs are limitless. Your digital persona is going to need clothing and accessories. You'll want tickets to in-world concerts and events. You might want to hang out in your virtual apartment in a digital city or a mansion in a digital paradise. And you'll want the right neighbors. Just ask the NFT collector who spent $450,000 on the virtual property next door to Snoop Dogg in Sandbox last fall—a sentence that might make a lot more sense in a few years than it does today.

While entertainment will play a significant role in the metaverse, social entrepreneur David Seigel argues that it will eventually become a space where people can share experiences online, be it a digital picnic with far-flung relatives or a global team collaborating on designs for a new airplane. If it reaches its full potential, the metaverse could make the concept of distance functionally irrelevant. Simply put on your VR headset and find yourself in a new environment entirely.

There are at least 150 companies currently working on building and expanding the hardware and software architecture to allow the metaverse to fulfill its potential. A few big names still dominate the field:

Meta/Facebook. In 2021, Facebook founder and CEO Mark Zuckerberg announced that the company was re-branding as Meta. He told the website The Verge that he believed over the next five years, "We will effectively transition from people seeing us as primarily being a social media company into being a metaverse company."

Epic Games. Epic Games runs the popular online game Fortnite and plans to expand into the metaverse. CEO Tim Sweeney told Bloomberg last fall that it's "kind of a race to get to a billion users, whoever brings on a billion users first would be the presumed leader in setting the standards." The company recently announced a $1 billion funding round to accelerate its efforts.

Nvidia. The computer chip giant has launched Omniverse, a tool that will allow developers to bring their virtual creations to life. The company recently announced that it was making access to the Omniverse platform free for individual users to push innovation in 3D simulations and designs.

Unity. Many believe that software developer Unity will come out on top of the heap in developing the metaverse. It has become an industry leader in real-time 3D content and is expanding its footprint in the development space. "We're very much in the awkward, 'everything is expensive, heavy, and doesn't work that well' [stage]," Unity's AR chief Timoni West tells Fast Company. "But give it another good 20 years and a reasonable amount of investment, and I think we'll bridge that gap and be in the next era of computing."

Building and managing the metaverse will take the work of tens of thousands—or hundreds of thousands—of new tech workers in the next five to 10 years. Industry experts say some of the most in-demand skills will be:

3D Game Designers – While the metaverse isn't meant to be a game, it will require many immersive design skills. Along with creative vision, animation skills, and basic programming skills, ITCareerFinder.com says designers will need programming experience with "popular gaming software programs such as Unity, Blender, Maya, and Unreal Engine."

AR/VR Software Engineers – While the metaverse, like legacy virtual worlds and gaming, will be available via computer, companies like Facebook and Microsoft are focusing more on developing the extended reality (XR) of virtual experiences: AR, VR, and mixed reality (MR). Programmers with experience in C, C++, JavaScript, Python, Unity, Unreal Engine, and other tools might find a home here, particularly if they also have a firm grasp of user experience (UX) concepts.

Hardware Engineers – The metaverse will be created in code, but it's meant to be experienced. Along with next-generation VR goggles and other visual aids, the technology is likely to spread out into a wide range of wearables that allow users to "feel" their environments. "And that's not even getting into the boring stuff, such as inertial measurement units, visual light cameras, depth cameras to help with tracking, localization..." writes Adrian Book at .cult, a platform specializing in tech developer news. This will take engineers with skills in everything from programming languages to haptics, robotics, and even AI.

Blockchain Engineers – The digital economy within the metaverse is likely to run on cryptocurrencies and NFTs, so those with skills in the design, implementation, and deployment of blockchain platforms will be much in demand.

These, of course, are just a sample of the types of jobs that will become available in the metaverse. Game designers, storytellers, digital marketing specialists, cyber security specialists, moderators, and even fashion designers will all have a role to play.

Experts say that those who decide to work within the metaverse will not only need top-notch technical skills but "soft" skills like the ability to collaborate, communicate, and adapt to ever-changing conditions. Emotional intelligence is going to count as much as tech savvy. You are going to be building a whole new world.

Tips for College or Trade School Students

Focusing on the appropriate majors and skills is crucial to future success and employment. Students majoring in computer science or information technology benefit from learning skills specific to the development and maintenance of the metaverse. In preparing for employment within the metaverse industry, college students and other job seekers should gain expertise and experience with popular programming languages, such as C, C#, C++, JavaScript, Python, etc. Likewise, gain expertise with popular tools like Unreal Engine, Unity, Amazon Sumerian, Autodesk Maya, and the open-source Blender. Having an eye on user experience design is also valuable because the result of metaverse development should be a user-friendly experience.

Another significant role in metaverse development is designing and creating 3D assets, typically a task for 3D game designers. Job applicants and students should seek expertise in designing, prototyping, and constructing immersive 3D experiences that engage players and immerse them in a virtual world like never before. Gaining a working knowledge of computer animation, 3D modeling, computer illustration, lighting, game interfaces, and creative competency for art and design is crucial to success as a 3D game designer. Basic programming skills in gaming software such as Unity, Blender, Maya, and Unreal Engine are core parts of 3D game design.

Are you looking to focus on the hardware side of the metaverse? A hardware systems engineer designs, prototypes, builds, and maintains the hardware that interfaces with the metaverse. They design AR/VR wearables and vital computer systems, such as servers, networks, and more. Gaining experience in product development, systems design, physics, and exposure to electrical, computer, mechanical, or optical engineering will all help set you apart from other candidates. Knowing virtual reality concepts and tools such as computer-aided design (CAD) and computer-aided engineering (CAE) will also give you a solid foundational skill set. Mastering the hardware and engineering side of the metaverse requires a lot of skill acquisition, so start with programming languages, data collection, analysis, and robotics—explicitly focusing on sensors, cameras, and user inputs.

As the metaverse's popularity and size grow, so will employment opportunities across all industries. If you're just starting out, you can choose a general path from the above list based on your interests. Then, prepare through college programs, internships, and, later, networking with experts in the metaverse itself.

Technical Skills vs. Soft Skills

The expansion of Web3 and the metaverse will bring a parallel expansion to IT departments in every industry and business. The career opportunities in information technology are a starting point for Black students looking to explore options that can take them from industry to industry, or metaverse to metaverse.

Information technology involves the use of computers to store, retrieve, transmit, and manipulate data. IT is typically used within the context of business operations as opposed to personal or entertainment technologies. An IT career centers on various responsibilities of a computer system—including all hardware, software, and peripheral equipment—operated by a specially trained group of users. If you're considering a career in information technology, you'll work in one of the core areas of responsibility of IT.

- IT governance involves the various policies and processes that ensure IT systems are effectively implemented and suit the needs of the company or service.
- IT operations cover the daily work of an IT department. This includes providing tech support, network maintenance, security testing, and device management.
- Hardware jobs involve all the physical components of the computer infrastructure. This pillar of IT centers upon the initial setup and ongoing maintenance of equipment such as servers, routers, phone systems, and individual devices like desktops, tablets, and laptops.

IT departments offer some of the following positions:
- Computer support specialists work with non-IT colleagues. They can be found troubleshooting any technology issues

including software problems, computer crashes, and trouble with hardware. Computer support specialists may also assist their senior-level IT colleagues (or supervisors) with larger-scale issues.

- Computer systems analysts work behind the scenes to marry IT with smart business solutions. They usually specialize in a particular industry—like finance or government—while working for a technology firm.

- Information security analysts are responsible for the security of their company's computer networks. They conduct tests and develop company-wide security practices to ensure that all employees are safely using the network and protecting their data.

- Computer network architects design and build data communication networks like local area networks, wide area networks, and intranets. Their typical job tasks include creating plans and layouts for networks, articulating designs with colleagues and management staff, and upgrading hardware and software to support current networks.

- Software developers create new and proprietary applications and systems that operate company devices, control company networks, and allow employees to complete specific tasks. Software developers speak with employees and customers in order to determine how new applications will meet their needs and function, while working closely with programmers and other IT team members.

When searching for employers, consider that some of these roles will change depending on the size and type of company. In smaller companies, daily work might focus on ordinary, mundane tasks like troubleshooting peripherals such as printers. In those environments, it is possible that you may be best suited to be more of a jack-of-all-trades tech who has broad skills and knowledge. With large companies, IT employees typically have a more diverse focus on the many facets of the organization itself. They may work upward into management and organizational planning roles, while other specialists may pursue more niche areas like cyber security.

The average salary range for IT positions spans from the low $80,000s to the mid-$100,000s. These competitive salaries are in line with the specialized skills and degrees that are required for employment, as a four-year degree and demonstrated skill proficiency is essential to obtaining employment.

In the next five to 10 years, expect more and more IT positions to focus on the following cutting-edge technologies, and more:

- Artificial intelligence
- Machine learning
- Robotic process automation
- Edge computing
- Quantum computing
- Virtual and augmented reality
- Blockchain
- 5G
- The Internet of Things

Entering into the information technology field will typically require a four-year degree in an academic area of study related to either computer science or computer information systems. If you are not planning on earning a four-year degree, you could enter this field by starting in an entry-level support role and proving your skills and growth potential. In rare cases, applicants can exhibit natural talent and skill in order to demonstrate employability. This oath, however, is not a standard means of entering the field. Earning a four-year degree should enable you to skip entry-level support roles and enter the job market in a junior-level support role in a given discipline.

One ongoing trend that has become more and more prevalent in recent years is the growing difficulty of obtaining an entry- or junior-level job without internships and/or a convincing demonstration of knowledge and skills. Internships, volunteer work, and industry certifications are all great ways of building your resume, demonstrating your commitment and expertise, and overcoming the barrier of being one of many qualified applicants for a specific job. A blend of hard skills and soft skills will ensure that you're an attractive applicant for job openings. Here are a few categories of skills or knowledge that will help set you on a firm path to work in the IT field.

Technical skills are necessary in the IT industry. While some may be obvious or in your existing capacity, some might surprise you—or be an area that needs improvement.

- Coding
- Technical writing
- Social media management
- Hardware deployment
- Network configuration
- Operating system knowledge
- Database management

One of the most essential skill sets an employer will look for in an IT professional is the applicant's proficiency in writing code. If you're looking for a job in programming or software and web development, an employer will most likely seek a qualified candidate who can read, write, and troubleshoot code in a variety of different languages because most systems utilize several languages.

Even for roles that are not tasked with writing code, an IT professional should have at least a working knowledge of the more basic coding languages, like HTML and C++. You'll want to evaluate which of the following you might need to better understand:

- Application development
- Architecture
- Artificial intelligence
- Cloud computing
- HTML
- C++
- C language
- PHP

- UX design
- Python
- JavaScript
- Java
- Ruby

In addition to programming languages, an understanding of computer networking will be required of most IT professionals, no matter the size of the company. IT jobs may include network architects, engineers, and systems administrators. Network administrators and systems administrators are responsible for the day-to-day operations of a larger network infrastructure and system. If you're looking to fulfill one of these roles, you'll need an understanding of the following:

- IP setup
- Wireless modems/routers
- Cloud services
- PHP
- SQL
- JavaScript
- Python
- C++
- Functionality
- Cyber security
- Information management
- Cloud systems administration

Along with technical skills, soft skills are important for anyone in IT. Specifically, communication skills are essential because information technology professionals are often required to work with or for many teams and groups of stakeholders. IT professionals often have to provide tech solutions for people who do not have a background in technology. This requires patience and understanding, as well as a positive outlook. IT professionals have to demonstrate leadership and team building at all levels of projects, and with many different types of people. Public speaking is also a valuable skill, as IT team members are often called on to present ideas and reports to larger groups of people, from colleagues all the way up to senior management. It's important to hone the following soft skills:

- Team building
- Teamwork
- Leadership
- Collaboration
- Written communication
- Oral communication
- Active listening
- Communicating complex information in digestible amounts

TAKEAWAYS
CHAPTER EIGHT

- MORE THAN 150 COMPANIES ARE CURRENTLY BUILDING AND EXPANDING THE HARDWARE AND SOFTWARE ARCHITECTURE TO ALLOW THE METAVERSE TO FULFILL ITS POTENTIAL

- FOCUS ON THE APPROPRIATE MAJORS AND SKILLS CRUCIAL TO FUTURE SUCCESS, SUCH AS PROGRAMMING LANGUAGES C, C++, JAVASCRIPT, PYTHON, ETC.

- GAIN EXPERIENCE WITH UNREAL ENGINE, UNITY, AMAZON SUMERIAN, AUTODESK MAYA, AND BLENDER.

- IN THE NEXT 10 YEARS, EXPECT MORE IT POSITIONS TO FOCUS ON AI, ML, ROBOTIC PROCESS AUTOMATION, EDGE COMPUTING, QUANTUM COMPUTING, VR, AR, AND BLOCKCHAIN.

- STAY FOCUSED ON USER EXPERIENCE DESIGN.

CHAPTER NINE:
The Next Wave of Change

History has shown us that our ability to continuously discover, build, and advance as a global society is critical to our sustainability as a species. The last few centuries have introduced quantum leaps in societal operations and understanding our limited resources in nature and our evolution as humanity itself in developing infrastructures and economies in support of humanity's well-being. With each wave of change, a group succeeds and propels forward, and a group is forced to remain stagnant.

The first wave of change came during the 19th century. The Industrial Revolution brought about coal-fired railroads and emerging national markets managed using steam-powered printing technology. During the 20th century, or the Second Industrial Revolution, electronic communications, radio, and television, were used to control and advertise the oil-powered automobile and mass consumer culture.

In the late 1990s, a new infrastructure was created using internet technology and renewable energy. The third Industrial Revolution aimed to alter the world through access to information. The World Wide Web (the Web) is one of the most important inventions in human history. It enables people to share information and ideas instantly and easily. Today, the Web plays an important role in almost every aspect of our lives. In fact, it has become so pervasive that many people use it as their primary source of information.

Without the introduction of the internet, we would not be poised to push the boundaries of Web3, Web4, and the metaverse. First-to-market companies are gaining competitive advantage insights in workplace innovation through next-gen technologies such as augmented reality

(AR) and virtual reality (VR) and further exploring their integration into new business models to drive margins up and costs down. To accomplish their market endeavors, they are quickly marshaling new and younger talent and other resources to drive new revenue opportunities in these emerging markets. Technology today, like in the past, gradually synthesizes the lives of the consumer in terms of quality of life and life conveniences; however, this same technology provides a pathway to wealth and prosperity for creators and producers of applications and services that meld our lives in the physical world with the metaverse.

The metaverse in these early innings of market adoption is on the path to becoming a mixed-reality virtual experience on multiple devices, connecting users worldwide. What was indicative of the internet as a market disruptor was the commoditization of information. The metaverse represents a social media and virtual experience distribution network where people can share experiences, media, things, thoughts, and ideas in an online forum where the physical and virtual world meet to create new experiences, insights and knowledge exchanges, and monetization opportunities. It is also a complex, virtual world that lets users walk, fly, and teleport around and experience different environments and thus provide a "platform of experiences" that turns discovery into lifelong learning and discovery opportunities.

We are witnessing an exciting innovation that offers endless pathways to interact with each other now and into the foreseeable future. And whatever form it takes, it's sure to provide plenty of opportunities for people to explore and learn.

It sounds like a dream, *doesn't it?*

It's important to note that, historically, when these societal shifts have occurred, Blacks and other underrepresented groups have often missed the train. This is due primarily to their station in society and the need to gain equal access to the resources, mind-share, and education ecosystems that spur innovation and technological advancements. We are now seeing the shaping of a new society that is no longer bound to the three-dimensional space we call the physical world. We can now create dimensions, perspectives, and their associated experiences that produce a Diversity-into-Action (real-time) market, and also experience insights through analytics.

The National Law Review (NLR) forewarned in March 2022 who the key players are in the metaverse patent race. According to the NLR, legacy tech companies have begun developing and patenting technologies to power the metaverse. Some of the proprietary technologies mentioned in the NLR article include "systems for optimizing shared views of virtual objects to multiple wearers of virtual reality (VR) headsets; algorithms for generating and moving virtual shapes and scenes in a VR environment based on hand gestures, head motion, or line of sight of the user; systems for generating haptic feedback as users interact with virtual objects; and methods for generating 3D avatars that mimic users' appearance and behavior."

According to a study published in *The Quarterly Journal of Economics* in 2018, white, male, and wealthy individuals hold the majority of U.S. patents. Another study from 2018 found that Black inventors received six patents per million people from 1970 to 2006, compared to over 40 patents per million for women and over 235 patents per million for all U.S. inventors. What are the implications for legacy tech companies regarding how many of their stakeholders are developers of color?

Time, historical revisionism, and the information age have shown us that Black innovators have significantly contributed and, with leadership, shaped and pushed our world further through all three waves of industrial change. The mailbox, traffic lights, elevator doors, the modern toilet, and even home security systems were all major contributions to the quality of life for all society by Black inventors.

According to Shontavia Jackson Johnson's "The Colorblind Patent System and Black Inventors," published by the American Bar Association, Lewis Latimer and Granville T. Woods were two of the most prolific 19th-century Black American innovators in electricity and telegraphic communications. Because today's Black innovators do not confront the same legal and societal obstacles in the patent system, many have succeeded. However, "Black U.S. patentees are disproportionately low," Johnson says.

The Metaquake is an opportunity for real change. It's time for those continuously marginalized by the digital divide to step up and out from the shadows and into the new frontier of the metaverse. But to do so will require action, commitment, and a desire to disrupt the status quo and evolve into a society that measures the value of its citizens based on new standards and ethics that measure contributions instead of differences.

We're not waiting for the Metaquake to happen—because the race to the metaverse is happening now. Other countries are already putting in plans of action to ensure their people are benefiting and leading this new territory.

Lessons from Overseas

In China, for example, the metaverse has become a new economic catalyst and has participation from investors, developers, and content creators. Several technology companies are developing metaverse-type apps and investing in the VR/AR segment of the metaverse. Six Chinese tech giants were named among the top 10 firms worldwide that filed the most VR/AR patent applications in the past two years.

Several Chinese software and service vendors have entered the AR market, and according to a recent report by Morgan Stanley, the Chinese metaverse market may be worth up to $8 trillion in the future. China has recently made a few moves to expand its metaverse imprint.

- Baidu launched a metaverse app in December 2021, which allowed users to engage in a virtual environment that combined Chinese history and futuristic designs.
- Tencent, the creator of WeChat, launched a 3D interactive space called Super QQ Show on the QQ platform.
- In 2022, an app called Jelly became the most downloaded app in China's iOS store, beating WeChat. Although it encountered delays and crashes, it still represents a valuable lesson for the tech giant.

- Byte Dance, the parent firm of TikTok, has designed two metaverse apps called Party Island and Pixsoul. These apps allow users to create virtual avatars and communicate with their friends.
- Ayayi, China's first meta-human, has already joined Alibaba as the digital manager of Tmall Super Brand.

China is not the only player racing toward the metaverse. The largest city in the UAE just announced a new metaverse strategy that aims to create 40,000 new jobs and attract 1,000 companies actively working to develop the metaverse.

Dubai's crown prince announced that Dubai would add $4 billion to its gross domestic product by investing in metaverse projects, an ambitious plan to attract 5,000 blockchain and metaverse companies by 2027. The Dubai Metaverse Strategy outlines a plan to foster metaverse innovation and economic contribution, cultivate metaverse talent, and develop metaverse use cases and applications within the Dubai government.

To the Cloud: Building a Metaverse Strategy

The Metaquake is the opportunity to create change—to ensure history does not repeat itself by broadening the inclusion to Black and brown communities nationally. How do we make this happen and ensure equal access to innovation opportunities? What does a metaverse strategy look like for the Black community and other minorities?

A tactical beginning is to identify the entry points for the Black community to become immersed in the present technology and receive training, development, and mentorship toward producing monetizable products, services, and applications. Thanks to the vast potential of the metaverse, tracking these types of opportunities, from technical and hardware to creative and strategic innovations, is a growing list.

Hardware is critical. Innovative people with access to hardware have driven each new technology cycle. Quantum mechanics and computers will continue to open opportunities for underserved communities to participate and advance our imaginations.

Nothing stops the creation of billion-dollar companies based on the existing infrastructure. What is new about the hardware market that is of interest to metaverse creators and producers is the maturing trends toward hardware-as-a-service and open-source hardware, which tremendously reduces the cost barrier of entry for digital twin experience design and development. Open-source hardware is yet another pathway toward extending the opportunities in the metaverse to digital, physical, and hybrid experiences.

The Meta Era has been driven by hardware innovations in hyperscale infrastructures and scalable infrastructures-on-demand through cloud providers. An additional value proposition is its ability to link people with hardware to interactive information, data, and processes. So, what do we need for digital opportunities to be open to underserved communities? The key is access to talent development, technology affordability, early-stage and angel funding, and market access to promote, sell, and grow the business.

An educated labor force is critical to the global economic vitality of the USA. The metaverse is all about team sports and giving everyone a platform in time and space to work collaboratively. Physical barriers are removed when playing in the metaverse.

That is what the STEM City USA Metaverse Strategy is all about. People, technology, funding, and market access mean little without a strategy.

The STEM City USA Strategy

I.   Develop and foster talent as early as possible

We've discussed the different routes students can take to work on their hard and soft skills for a career in the metaverse. We've also looked at what steps our educational institutions are taking toward creating a solid pipeline for talent. Now it's time to fuse a connection.

At STEM City USA, we are working on building an intellectual pipeline through partnerships with HBCUs and Hispanic-serving institutions. HBCUs are already moving toward integrating the metaverse into their curriculums and student-life experiences. Morehouse College announced a new metaverse campus offering a unique student option for interaction. In April 2022, EON Reality, the global leader in AR and VR learning solutions for industry and education, and Clark Atlanta University announced a partnership to bring the Knowledge Metaverse to the HBCU community.

The Thurgood Marshall College Fund (TMCF) Campus ONE MetaScholars Program was launched to educate HBCU students and bring them up to speed as we transition from in-person experiences to virtual experiences inside of the metaverse.

The most vital piece to this pipeline will be educators. The need for qualified metaverse experts and innovators available to teach and guide students through these institutions will continue to grow as our use of the metaverse expands. College programs geared toward computer engineering and IT also need to evolve to meet the needs of the metaverse, providing more robust programs in AI, machine learning, and 3D designs. College electives and courses need to expand to include metaverse ecosystem offerings and educate the value of the metaverse to other majors like marketing, sales, computer science, biology, history, literature, etc. There is a unique opportunity to characterize 21st-century learning in the metaverse.

II. Building the expandable platform that allows the creation of the digital twin experience

A metaverse with endless possibilities needs a platform with endless possibilities. The next step to the platform is funneling talent into a space where they can apply their skills and create meaningful connections within the metaverse. STEM City USA is a browser-based platform that loads instantly and gives multi-users live data and coherent experiences.

The platform allows communities and organizations to create open metaverses, enabling them to hop from world to world. The possibilities are limitless for collaboration. Schools, colleges, and research departments are available in STEM City to connect members worldwide.

III. Defining the opportunities

As more people come to see the metaverse not just as a futuristic concept but as an imminent opportunity for investment and collaboration, we need to ensure that there are opportunities for underrepresented communities in this new space too. These technologies will also allow entrepreneurs to connect with one another, collaborate on ideas, and start new businesses from home. The creator economy will also continue to grow as content creation and brand endorsements will shift toward the metaverse.

Currently, less than 10 percent of Black businesses generate more than $1 million. And even though 20 percent of Black Americans start their own business, only 4 percent survive the startup stage. The Metaquake is an opportunity to change these statistics.

A recent Engineering Industry Economic Contribution research study reveals the critical role of engineering and design services. Every additional $1 of revenue in engineering and design services contributes $1.55 to the U.S. GDP. In addition to the two supporting sectors for each new job created in the engineering sector, the sector contributed nearly 3 percent of the U.S. GDP in 2019.

The creation and expansion of the metaverse will bring higher demand for skilled talent into companies looking to pioneer the space. Pair that with increased consumer demand, and we can safely predict revenue upwards of $1 trillion with the addition of Blacks and Hispanics into the talent pipeline.

IV. Building the provider network

Community and elected officials' support is crucial to a successful metaverse ecosystem. Accountability across both the private and public sectors will help us bridge the digital divide and bring metaverse opportunities to underrepresented communities. STEM City USA actively works with elected officials and high-ranking minority leaders at government agencies to work toward accomplishing a common goal to bring our society into the future without marginalizing our bottom line.

We will start to see a shift in how the public and private sectors interact with their communities. For example, the metaverse will bring about a new recruitment and training method for military programs, and health care access can change dramatically through facilities in the metaverse. These are just some of the examples of seismic shifts we'll experience through a cohesive metaverse ecosystem.

Proactive Metaverse Conversations: A Collective Conscience

This strategy is only as good as our action moving forward. Thankfully, the conversation doesn't stop with the closing of this chapter. We can continue to build, create, and expand a metaverse experience for every underrepresented community through active conversations and participation. This is where you come in.

Meet us in the city in the sky, STEM City USA, to experience for yourself the endless opportunities we, as a community, can create together. You can use the QR codes in this book to go straight into STEM City USA, where you can access expanded information referenced in this book, speakers and scholars' profiles, and group forums to discuss the Metaquake, contribute ideas, and make connections to get involved in the creation of the metaverse.

I want to emphasize that *Metaquake USA: The Metaverse and How It Will Shape Your Future* is a living document and collection of the metaverse resources and strategy for Black and underrepresented communities. It is my goal, and that of everyone involved in the conversations referenced in this book, to keep the conversation pushing forward and continuously bring access to information and ideas about our place in the metaverse.

The time is now. The Metaquake is here.

Are you ready to join the journey?

DR. KEVIN KORNEGAY

CLOSING REMARKS

by Dr. Kevin Kornegay

Tyrone Taborn's book *Metaquake* presents a comprehensive overview of the metaverse and its impact on Black communities. It provides an insightful historical perspective of technology, which is key to understanding its importance to our future. The book highlights the specific and significant contributions we have made in the digital world, in particular, the work by Mark Dean, Dr. Colin Parris, and other notable visionaries. We all must recognize and understand where we've been before knowing where we are going. Many people don't know about these pioneers, but they should. To get the profound perspectives of these visionaries regarding the significance of the metaverse—and to capture them all in one place—is nothing short of amazing. That is the power of *Metaquake*. It is a perfectly-timed publication that defines the roles Black populations can (and should) play in the current digital revolution.

The simple but imperative message of the book is this: The time to get involved in the technology evolution is now. We need to wake up, find our space and place, and get involved. As pervasive as technology is today, with many Black households utilizing smart televisions and devices, we have no room for excuses. Technology permeates every aspect of our daily lives, and the metaverse will be no different.

Beneficially, participation is a part of a significant socio-economic movement. We cannot miss the opportunity to put our stamp on and in this universe with unparalleled voices, one-of-a-kind creativity, and extraordinary ideologies. Neither can we afford to miss out on the many advantages and benefits the metaverse will offer, the biggest of which is the shared collective experience. Shared experience in this digital space will be more important, in my opinion, than reality because people will be able to create their own realities—a privilege Black people have been denied throughout history. To have the opportunity and space to amplify our voices and create our own reality is not only liberating, but it is also empowering.

Detrimentally, if the metaverse is developed further without our participation, engagement, or involvement, we will see a greater divide between the "haves" and the "have-nots." Tyrone Taborn highlights the potential cultural and economic pitfalls that would undoubtedly occur should Black people miss out on this tremendous moment or decide not to participate. Make no mistake: There are many forces at play when it comes to the late deployment of technology in underserved communities. We have to fight for inclusion in these technologies! We have tremendous economic power, so we should leverage that power to demand our seats at the table when they decide zoning for these new technologies and deployment. We need to be the alpha sites of deployment versus the suburban neighborhoods, and Tyrone Taborn's exceptional book provides the blueprint to do so efficiently and expeditiously.

The Metaquake is upon us, and the onus to take our rightful, deserved place in this next digital evolution is on each individual. Kudos and sincerest thanks to Tyrone Taborn for such a provoking and enlightening commentary.

THE
STEM CITY USA
STRATEGY

- DEVELOP AND FOSTER TALENT AS EARLY AS POSSIBLE

- BUILD THE EXPANDABLE PLATFORM THAT ALLOWS THE CREATION OF THE DIGITAL TWIN EXPERIENCE

- DEFINE THE OPPORTUNITIES

- BUILD THE PROVIDER NETWORK

ACKNOWLEDGEMENTS

Thanks to STEM City Press for selecting *Metaquake USA* as one of the first books published under the STEM City Press imprint. STEM City Press is a pioneering extension of the STEM City USA Metaverse platform. STEM City Press has one goal: to assist underrepresented scholars in getting their research published as rapidly as possible.

Creating a publishing house for journals and books was the dream of the late Dr. Gary L. Harris. Gary and I were classmates at Cornell University, where he was one of the first African Americans to obtain a Ph.D. in electrical engineering, along with Dr. Michael Spencer. Dr. Harris felt that minority scholars and those writing about issues that impact the Black community encountered many barriers to publishing. STEM City Press is now the fulfillment of that dream.

This book started on the STEM City USA metaverse platform with virtual interviews recorded for my Metaquake USA talk series. That was intentional. We wanted our first book about the metaverse to start in the metaverse while showing the endless capabilities to network virtually with a focus on social connection. This book is a proof of concept.

I want to thank Dr. Eugene DeLoatch, Dean Emeritus, Clarence M. Mitchell, Jr. School of Engineering, Morgan State University; Congressman Kweisi Mfume (D), 7th Congressional District; and Baltimore media personality Marc Clarke for encouraging me to take the first steps.

But to get here, we needed to build STEM City USA, one of the first web-based metaverses. No one was more instrumental in bringing STEM City USA to life than Beverly Wladkowski, the art director at Career Communications Group (CCG). Beverly worked on every part of the STEM City USA concept from day one when I showed her my idea sketched on a napkin. I want to thank Stacy Bowles for helping to make the vision a reality.

I also want to praise my technology think tank, BEYA's Scientist of the Year Ernest Smiley and my go-to technologist, Jem Pagen. These two individuals continue to be the foundation of my technical thinking.

Then there was my *Metaquake* production team. They include Rayondon Kennedy (CCG managing editor), Bryan Davis (CCG digital director), Montez Miller (CCG Producer), and Nikkie Stevens (CCG communications and sourcing specialist).

Writing a book like this has been a team effort. I want to thank my advisory team, starting with a decades-long collaborator, Lango Deen; Professor William U'Ren, a veteran film adaptation specialist; and Jessica Rafaeil, a PR and branding specialist.

Finally, I doubt I could have completed this project without my wife, Jean Hamilton.

In memory of
DR. GARY L. HARRIS

ABOUT THE AUTHOR
Tyrone D. Taborn

Tyrone D. Taborn is the publisher and CEO of Career Communications Group (CCG), a multicultural media services company that connects diverse talent in STEM fields to leading employers and opportunities. Since its incorporation in 1981, CCG has built lasting partnerships with top companies, U.S. government agencies, and educational institutions through its annual conferences, magazines, and the STEM City USA metaverse—all to promote the achievements of minorities in STEM and inspire the next generation of innovators.

Taborn is also the creator of the Foundation for Educational Development, which aims to raise awareness of STEM career opportunities. The foundation's programs include the Black Family Technology Awareness Week, La Familia Technology Awareness Week, and The Native American Family Technology Journey. Taborn contributed to the book *Learning Race and Ethnicity, Youth and Digital Media,* funded by the MacArthur Foundation and published by MIT Press. He is also the author of "Closing the Racial Digital Divide," one of 10 essays *in The Covenant with Black America* (Third World Press), a 2006 *New York Times* bestseller compiled by Tavis Smiley. In 2019, the National Science Board (NSB) honored Taborn for his exemplary service in promoting public understanding of science and engineering. The Historymakers recognized Taborn as an influential historical figure who has significantly impacted the Black community.

Photo captions appear on the following page

PHOTOS
from page 110

Undated photos featuring Career Communications Group publisher and CEO Tyrone Taborn with:

1. COLIN POWELL (1937-2021) WAS THE FORMER CHAIRMAN OF THE JOINT CHIEFS OF STAFF FROM OCTOBER 1, 1989, TO SEPTEMBER 30, 1993.

2. MARILLYN HEWSON, FORMER CHAIRMAN, PRESIDENT, AND CEO OF LOCKHEED MARTIN, DAVID L. STEWARD, CHAIRMAN AND FOUNDER OF WORLD WIDE TECHNOLOGY (WWT) AND 2012 BLACK ENGINEER OF THE YEAR.

3. VICE PRESIDENT KAMALA HARRIS.

4. (L-R) KWEISI MFUME, U.S. REPRESENTATIVE FOR MARYLAND'S 7TH CONGRESSIONAL DISTRICT; WILLIAM H. MURPHY JR., FORMER JUDGE IN BALTIMORE, MD; WES MOORE, 2022 GOVERNOR-ELECT OF MARYLAND; AND RADIO TALK HOST, LARRY YOUNG.

5. LLOYD J. AUSTIN III, CURRENTLY THE 28TH SECRETARY OF DEFENSE, WAS SWORN IN ON JAN. 22, 2021.

6. MICHELLE OBAMA, THE FIRST LADY OF THE UNITED STATES FROM 2009 TO 2017 (CENTER), AND JEAN HAMILTON, PRESIDENT AND CFO OF CAREER COMMUNICATIONS GROUP.

7. (L-R) 1997 BLACK ENGINEER OF THE YEAR ARTHUR E. JOHNSON, 1990 BLACK ENGINEER OF THE YEAR ARLINGTON W. CARTER, 1991 BLACK ENGINEER OF THE YEAR AND FIRST AMERICAN BLACK TO GO INTO SPACE, GUION "GUY" STEWART BLUFORD, AND 2000 BLACK ENGINEER OF THE YEAR MARK E. DEAN.

8. JEAN HAMILTON, PRESIDENT AND CFO OF CAREER COMMUNICATIONS GROUP, AND CHRIS ROCK, AMERICAN STAND-UP COMEDIAN, ACTOR, AND FILMMAKER (CENTER).

STEM USA CITY™

www.stemcityusa.com

BOOKSTORE

AUDITORIUM